D1596932

Conquest of Space

The earth as seen from Apollo 8 during the return flight. The North Pole is at the top of the picture, just left of centre. South America is in the middle, and North America at the far left.

Erich Dolezal

Conquest of Space

Translated from the German by Alfred Kurti

Illustrated with photographs

ABELARD - SCHUMAN
London   New York   Toronto

Cover photograph by Panorama Press

Photographs: Panorama Press, Zollofiken,
USIS and Novosti Agency

LONDON	NEW YORK	TORONTO
Abelard-Schuman	Abelard-Schuman	Abelard-Schuman
Limited	Limited	Canada Limited
8 King Street	6 West 57 Street	Scarborough
W.C.2	New York 10019	Ontario

Contents

Foreword by Wernher von Braun

Only a few more years will pass before mankind's age-old dream of reaching the brightly shining heavenly bodies is achieved. The extremely complex space vehicles and the enormous booster rockets necessary for carrying our Astronauts to the moon and providing them on such a voyage with a small piece of terrestrial environment, are already under construction. Even today the log book of manned space flight shows nearly 24 million miles of flight—truly an impressive total, especially if one realizes what a tremendous amount of technical development, work and preparation is required for the construction and launching of each individual manned space vehicle.

However, so far we have been limited in the case of all manned space travel projects to ballistic trajectories and satellite orbits because if we wish to escape from the gravitational field of the earth in manned space vehicles, we need much larger carrier rockets than those tested and used up to now. Whereas for the first ballistic flights of a Mercury capsule an advanced Redstone rocket, weighing approximately thirty tons at lift-off was adequate, our Saturn V rocket, at present undergoing tests and intended to carry the Apollo spaceship to the moon, will have a launch weight of approximately 2,819 tons, in other words, it will be ninety-four times as heavy. This is because it will have to carry the weight of the space cabin and its three-man crew into a transfer orbit to the moon and it must also carry sufficient fuel for the Apollo spaceship's safe return to earth. In addition, the moon-landing system planned by us requires a special lunar excursion module for descending to the moon's surface and subsequent take off into a circumlunar orbit followed by a rendezvous maneuver with the Apollo re-entry vehicle which has remained in orbit round the moon. To be able to satisfy these requirements with regard to thrust and payload, the moon rocket must be able to accelerate the Apollo spaceship, which together with all accessories weighs approximately 45 tons, to the required escape velocity of 6·7 miles per second.

These figures and data show clearly what tremendous forces are involved in the launching of a moon rocket. They also show what enormous technical problems will have to be solved for such an enterprise—let us consider for example the difficulties connected with the control of the huge forces and extremely high and low temperatures and pressures, as well as the attainment of maximum velocities within very narrow control limits.

This book is an excellent guide for all those who wish to learn something about the dynamic progress made in rocket and space technology during the past few years and to see how the idea of space travel has been transformed from fantasy and fanciful visions into a clearly defined field of action for science and technology. It describes the epoch-marking work and achievements of the early pioneers of space travel who, as ingenious individualists were not afraid to stand up for their daring ideas and convictions, independently of prevailing opinions and the views of their contemporaries.

The book describes the first high-altitude rocket flights in the service of science, the sensational launchings of the first artificial instrument satellites, the development program and tasks of commercial satellites, moon and planetary probes, and finally the epoch-marking advances of manned space vehicles into the regions beyond the earth's atmosphere which we have all followed with the greatest excitement.

Beyond that, this book presents a clear picture of the tasks confronting space research in the coming years and decades. I am certain that it will awaken in many readers not only an understanding of the subject, but also a lasting enthusiasm for space travel which will enable twentieth-century man to employ his unquenchable thirst for knowledge and desire to achieve great things in the exploration of increasingly distant space targets in his search for truth in God's infinite creation.

Wernher von Braun

First Came the Dream

". . . Ten twenty-nine," said Nicholl. "More than five minutes to go yet!" replied Barbicane.

"Yes, five short minutes," repeated Michel Ardan. "And we are enclosed in a projectile within a nine-hundred-foot-long gun. And underneath this projectile there are 181 tons of guncotton as powerful as 725 tons of ordinary gunpowder. And our friend Murchison, with the chronometer in his hand, not taking his eyes off the pointer, with his finger on the electrical contact, is counting the seconds, ready to fire us into interplanetary space!"

"That is enough, Michel, enough," Barbicane said in a serious tone of voice. "Let us get ready. Only a few moments remain until the last one. Give me your hands, my friends."

"Yes." Michel Ardan showed more emotion than he wanted to betray. The three men linked hands.

"May God protect us," said the devout Barbicane.

Michel Ardan and Nicholl stretched out on the cushions in the middle of the floor.

"Ten forty-seven," murmured the Captain. "Only twenty seconds!" Barbicane quickly extinguished the gas flame and lay down beside his comrades.

The silence was broken only by the chronometer beating the seconds.

Then . . . a terrible jolt, and the projectile, flung upward by 13,000 million gallons of gas, flew off into space . . .

This is how Jules Verne imagined the launching of a manned spaceship to the moon in 1864—over a century ago. Two eccentric Americans, an adventurous Frenchman and two dogs allow themselves to be shot to the moon from a nine-hundred-foot-long gun.

Today, any schoolboy would laugh at the idea of allowing oneself to be shot to the moon in a projectile (with gas light!) However, we must bear in mind that each age has its own engineering concepts and Jules Verne was very daring to dream of a journey to the moon at a time when there was no Cape Kennedy and no multistage carrier rocket.

The first journey to the moon of which we have any knowledge was described by the Greek author Lucian of Samosata, born in A.D. 125. The hero of his story sailed in a ship over the Pillars of Hercules, then regarded as the end of the world. There his ship was caught by a whirlwind and lifted to a spherical, illuminated island in space, the moon. Far below the sailors saw the earth with its towns, rivers and mountains. Does this not remind one of the descriptions given by our present-day Astronauts?

The French author Cyrano de Bergerac (1619–1655) did not choose such a simple way as Lucian. In Bergerac's journey to the moon, the laws of aviation are already anticipated. The hero of the story is lifted heavenward by bottles strapped to his body and containing dew which is raised by the heat of the sun, while the earth spins away from below him.

It was left to the writers of our technical age to endow their dreams of space travel at least with an appearance of scientific possibility. In the case of Jules Verne it was a gun. The English author H. G. Wells, in his novel *First Men in the Moon* (1901) made a professor invent a substance capable of screening gravity. That was at the beginning of our century. A short time before, the book *On Two Planets* by the German author Kurd Lasswitz, a mathematics teacher, created a sensation. This book describes the visit to earth of technically highly advanced Martians, whose spaceships were made of "Stellit," a material which can be made permeable to gravity. Lasswitz propelled his spaceships by "directional fire" and he thus anticipated engineering realities of today, by utilizing reaction.

A quarter of a century later, Otto Willi Gail wrote his book *Shot into Space* at a time when some, though only a few, men of science and engineering were seriously thinking about space travel. He described in a highly dramatic manner the launching of a rocket-propelled multistage spaceship. Let us turn the pages of this book which was enthusiastically read by young people of that time:

". . . disconnect alcohol rocket!" said Korf, speaking with difficulty.

The ship divided for the second time. The pure hydrogen rocket ignited and shot its fiery vapours downward with incredible speed.

The pointer came dangerously close to the red mark. The machine developed its maximum power.

Only five minutes had passed since the launching, an eternity for the crew. The roar of the exhaust had stopped and "Geryon" was racing through altitude where the tremendously rarefied air was no longer able to conduct sound.

They had to keep going for only another three minutes before the velocity was reached that would carry the ship beyond the earth's field of gravity. The speed indicator climbed steadily—23,000–26,000 feet per second.

Korf was struck by a dreadful thought: what would happen if he were unable to muster enough strength to pull the accelerator back?

This would mean that as a result of the high rate of acceleration, the speed would continue to increase and increase until the extensive reserves of the hydrogen rocket were exhausted. And then, devoid of all means of propulsion, there would be no return. The ship would be propelled beyond the earth's orbit. It would race at incredible speed into planetary space along a hyperbolic path whose branch would lead into the infinite. Less than half an hour to go before the velocity would be reached that would carry the ship away forever from the solar system.

The seventh minute had passed. The speeding ship now travelled 29,000 feet every second.

Slowly and with a groan Korf raised his arm. Weak from exhaustion he rested it in a sling suspended from the ceiling; his fingers were only a palm's width away from the control lever. With great effort Korf struggled for every inch, and his strength threatened to desert him. He stopped for a moment, exhausted.

The instrument showed relentlessly a speed of 29,000 feet per second.

"Oh God, only two seconds left!" With a jolt his hand gripped the handle, and the lever flew back. Korf's forehead was bathed in cold sweat; the terrible effort had used up the last remnants of his strength.

The accelerometer dropped, passed the twenty mark, dropped past

11

ten and came to rest at a speed increase of ten feet per second. The pressure disappeared—as suddenly as it had arisen. The chronometer indicated eight minutes . . .

The author, who showed a great deal of scientific knowledge, had taken into account many points still valid today but he was not able to foresee everything. The reality of a manned space flight (slightly more than a third of a century later) was by no means as dramatic as described by Otto Willi Gail. This does not mean, however, that it is any less exciting. We can see this for ourselves if we read a report about Gordon Cooper's space flight on May 15, 1963:

> . . . Only one more minute before launching. T minus 35 seconds. The "umbilical cords," supplying power from the ground station to the capsule are jettisoned and the Astronaut confirms by radio that he has now switched over to his own power unit. T minus 18 seconds! Now the final decision as to whether to continue or abandon the launching has to be made. The unanimous decision is "launch" and the automatic ignition system is switched on. The Astronaut leans back in his form-fitting couch and counts together with Schirra: "Ten . . . nine . . . eight. . . ."
> He is watching the instrument panel, constantly looking out for any changes in the light signals. He knows that dozens of technicians at the control positions of the ground station are doing the same. Should anything go wrong during these critical seconds, the control engineer can still switch off the booster rocket.
> "Three . . . two . . . one. . . ."
> "Ignition! "
> Cooper can feel the flames shooting out from the three nozzles of the combustion chambers of the "Atlas" rocket far below. Then he hears a distant noise similar to a thunder clap, indicating that the motors have reached their full power. The booster rocket lifts off. The gantries which had secured the "Atlas" to the launch platform, move back and Cooper is suspended in midair for a moment. The launching is very gentle. There is slight vibration but by no means as bad as he had expected.
> The gravity acceleration "g" increases rapidly and reaches a

U.S. Astronaut Major Leroy Gordon Cooper who was launched into space on May 15, 1963.

maximum of 8g. Vibration and noise are more severe now but the flight proceeds smoothly.

Within 131 seconds of launching the two booster engines cut out and are jettisoned exactly according to schedule. The spaceship has now reached an altitude of approximately forty miles and its distance from Cape Canaveral is approximately forty-five miles. Its present speed is approximately 8,800 feet per second. Further propulsion is now provided only by the main rocket motor whose nozzle emits a powerful jet of white-hot gas. The rocket speeds the Astronaut farther and farther skyward and he feels as if he were at the nose of a projectile accurately aimed at a specific point—the place where the spaceship changes course to enter into orbit. And then this moment has arrived. The acceleration pressure has ceased, the capsule separates from the rocket, and for the first time Cooper switches on the hydrogen peroxide attitude control rockets. The capsule turns and he looks out through the porthole; he sees the silvery shining rocket casing quite near; it is still surrounded by a belt of frozen oxygen about its middle. He can clearly read the inscription on the side.

The time is 19 hours 11 minutes, Local Time and he is at an altitude of 100 miles above Bermuda. His heart beat is very rapid, 150 beats per minute, but as soon as he becomes aware of this, it goes back to normal.

Through the headphones he hears Schirra's voice: "Great thing, eh?" All he can answer is: "You bet!" He feels almost in his subconscious mind that the major part of his life was a preparation for this moment.

This is how in our day and age an ancient dream, cherished by mankind, was fulfilled; it should be remembered that contrary to so many of our modern achievements, such as, for example, radio, television, electricity, photography, etc., space travel was thought about thousands of years ago.

Launch of an Atlas Rocket carrying a Mercury capsule with the American Astronaut into space.

It was Hard for the Pioneers

Even today there are still many people who think they know everything; the difference is that in matters of space travel, such people have become very cautious indeed. Before the first artificial satellites were placed in orbit around the earth by powerful rockets, some of these ultra-clever people often said with a condescending smile: "That is all well and good, but in a vacuum the rocket cannot move because it has nothing to push against." Any reasonably bright boy could in turn reply with a condescending smile: "Isaac Newton knew better nearly three hundred years ago. It is unfortunate, however, that the fireworks rockets which were known at that time did not fly out into space because otherwise people would have realized earlier that rockets do not need any air to push against. The rocket has the substance against which it pushes on board. If the hot combustion gases leave the nozzle of the rocket at high speed, they cause a reaction which is completely independent of whether the rocket is ignited in a vacuum or in an air-filled space."

Today this is no longer doubted by any reasonable person but many otherwise well-informed people admit honestly that although reality has shown that rockets can work in space, they cannot visualize a rocket working in a vacuum. However, before it became possible for rocket engineers to convince the last of the doubters, determined pioneers had to fight a hard battle which at times even seemed hopeless.

The firmament of space-travel pioneers is illuminated by a triple star: the Russian Tsiolkovski, the American Goddard and the German Oberth.

Konstantin Eduardovich Tsiolkovski was one of the earliest pioneers of space travel. He was born in 1857 in the small village of Ievsk in the Province of Ryazan. His father was a forestry worker. At the age of ten, Tsiolkovski lost his hearing as a result of scarlet fever. The boy's perception, however, became extremely acute. He withdrew almost entirely from his surroundings and lived only for his studies.

16

His passion was mathematics and physics. And so he started dreaming about the stars. For three years he studied physics, astronomy, mechanics and geometry in Moscow. As a child he was once given a balloon and the memory of this had a lasting effect on him. Flying was his dream although his thoughts turned not only to flying in the air, but far beyond in space. His scientific studies, combined with a lively imagination, resulted in great determination. He recognized quite clearly that the rocket principle, which in turn is based on the law of conservation of the center of mass, represents the key to space travel.

The pale, deaf and hungry student was overwhelmed by the realization that the center of mass of our planet would continue along its path without change even if a tremendous explosion were to blow it up into thousands of fragments flying away in all directions. The center of mass remains unchanged as long as only internal forces are active. A grenade fired from a gun travels along its trajectory. If it explodes in mid-flight, the center of mass of the diverging splinters will continue undisturbed along its original path. This means that if the combustion gases of a rocket leave the nozzle at high speed, the remainder of the rocket, its casing, must move in the opposite direction in order to prevent the threatened displacement of the center of mass. This invariable law must be obeyed everywhere, even in empty space. Tsiolkovski recognized immediately that the available fuels (in those days rockets were mostly propelled by gunpowder) were completely inadequate for overcoming the earth's gravitational pull.

In 1882 Tsiolkovski was appointed teacher at the District School in Borovsk near Kaluga. At long last he was able to think about writing down his ideas. He had attracted the attention of scientific circles and in 1892 he was appointed teacher at the Kaluga Technical College. In 1898 Tsiolkovski had completed his first comprehensive work about the possibility of space travel. Its title was: *The Exploration of Space by means of Reaction Devices.* He submitted it to the editorial offices of the *Scientific Review* in Moscow but it was not published until five years later. He was the first research worker to recognize the significance of the multistage principle and of liquid propellants for efficient and powerful rockets.

Tsiolkovski published further articles on the subject of space travel. They were all written in Russian and published in periodicals virtually unknown outside Russia. This saved him a great deal of bother because Russian experts did not object to these milestones along the road into space, and the outside world knew nothing of their existence. As a result, Tsiolkovski's name became internationally known only at a time when others had pushed open the gateways to the stars. Tsiolkovski died on September 19, 1935; he was unable to witness the triumph of his ideas but shortly before his death, on May 1, 1933, he spoke the following prophetic words: "I have now been working on the rocket principle for forty years and all the time I have firmly believed that a flight to the planet Mars will be possible within the foreseeable future. Only times change but ideas remain. Today I am convinced that many of you will witness an interplanetary flight."

How quickly these words have come true! Credit for this must go above all to two men: Robert Hutchins Goddard and Hermann Oberth. Goddard was born on October 5, 1882 in Worcester, Massachusetts. He devoted himself to the study of physics, reaching the position of university professor in this field. He was greatly interested in the history of rockets and found that throughout the Middle Ages and during the early part of modern times many more rocket experiments were carried out and far more had been written about them than is generally assumed today.

In 1912 he held in his hand for the first time sea-rescue rockets used for shooting lifelines to ships in distress. Goddard discovered very soon that only approximately three per cent. of the energy in the propellant was utilized by those rockets. This was of great interest to him as a physicist and he started to make calculations; he found that the shape of the nozzle and the configuration of the rocket were especially in need of improvement. He also started experimenting with powder rockets and, in 1919, he published the results of his theoretical and practical investigations under the title *A Method of Reaching Extreme Altitudes*. This work was written in a very dry, scientific style and was of interest only to experts. And yet, its contents were a veritable sensation: for the first time a man of science had dealt with the possibility of sending an unmanned rocket to the moon. He wrote:

For my experiments I generally used a powder having an energy content of 1,238·5 calories per kilogram. Using this powder would enable one to 'shoot' to the moon a device with a payload of one kilogram and a total weight, including fuel and dead weight, of 599 kilograms. Its arrival there could be indicated by arranging for the payload, which of course would have to arrive at new moon, to consist of an easily ignited flare such as, for example, magnesium. The flash of light generated on impact, which would last for several seconds if a suitable amount of magnesium were carried, could be observed from earth through a powerful telescope and could thus signal the successful arrival of the rocket at our earth satellite.

What in the case of Jules Verne was still pure fiction, had become a technical possibility with Goddard. Like Tsiolkovski, Goddard recognized the inadequacy of solid propellants. He was the first to recognize a further, essential fact. It would be extremely difficult to overcome the earth's gravitational pull with a single rocket. Goddard proposed the combination of several rockets, had this solution protected by patent, and so became the inventor of the multistage principle which is of such decisive importance for space travel.

From 1920 onward, Goddard experimented with liquid propellants. Finally he used petrol and liquid oxygen and on November 1, 1923 the world's first rocket motor driven by liquid propellants, operated at Goddard's test site in Auburn, Massachusetts. On March 16, 1926 his work had progressed to the stage where it became possible to launch the first liquid-propellant rocket. It flew for two and a half seconds and covered a distance of 184 feet. It was a modest beginning but a decisive one.

The problem of stabilizing the rocket presented Goddard with great difficulties; but he was able to solve that problem, too, and in May, 1935 a rocket with liquid propellants thundered into a blue sky from the Mescalero Ranch in New Mexico where Goddard had been able to establish a test site. The rocket rose to an altitude of 7,220 feet and reached a speed of 547 miles per hour. The problem of the liquid-propellant rocket and its stabilization had been solved.

Like Tsiolkovski, the modest professor who shunned all publicity did not live to see the day when space travel had become reality. He died on August 10, 1945. Just as Tsiolkovski's work received little attention outside Russia, Goddard's name remained unknown in Europe until the idea of space travel was helped toward its final breakthrough by the third great pioneer.

Hermann Oberth was born on June 25, 1894, the son of a doctor in the small town of Schässburg in Transylvania, at that time part of the Austrian Empire. His father wanted him to become a doctor, but the boy was much more interested in mathematics and physics. After reading Jules Verne's *From the Earth to the Moon* in his early youth, he became interested in rockets travelling into interplanetary space. Oberth's life shows that a book read during a man's youth can

A V2 (its technical designation is A4) during refuelling at the White Sands Proving Ground in New Mexico (U.S.A.)

determine the course of his life. He spent the last three years of his studies in Heidelberg where he gained a teaching diploma. That was in 1923. During his student days he had thought deeply about the problem of space travel and recorded his ideas in a highly scientific paper. However, all the publishers to whom he submitted it returned it with regret: they did not trust the calculations. After having unsuccessfully approached about twenty publishers, Oberth was on the point of giving up. Through the intervention of an acquaintance, the manuscript was finally submitted to the Munich publisher Rudolf Oldenbourg in 1922.

Launch of the first American two-stage rocket on February 24, 1949. It reached an altitude of more than 250 miles.

Left: Launch of a Jupiter C rocket carrying Explorer I at its nose.

Right: Launch of a Tiros satellite by means of a Thor-Able rocket, carrying the meteorological satellite into a circular orbit.

He was rather taken aback when he read the first page which began with four self-confident sentences:

1. At the present state of science and technology it is possible to construct machines capable of rising beyond the limits of the earth's atmosphere.

2. With further perfection, such machines can achieve velocities high enough to insure that these machines, left to themselves in the ether, will not fall back to the earth's surface and even be able to travel beyond the earth's gravitational field.

3. Machines of this type can be built in such a manner that human beings can travel in them, probably without any harmful effects on their health.

4. Given certain economic conditions, the construction of such machines may be a paying proposition. Such conditions could occur within a few decades.

It is almost uncanny how future developments confirmed the correctness of Oberth's four points. However, the publisher could not know that at the time; although he decided to publish the manuscript, he did so on condition that Oberth pay for the cost of printing.

To the great surprise of author and publisher (the book was published in 1923 under the title *The Rocket Into Interplanetary Space*) it was a great success. The first edition was sold out within a short time but Oberth's delight at this was tempered with the bitter experience of having to deal with stubborn sceptics and know-alls.

Oberth submitted his work—today considered the classical work on space travel—as a doctor's thesis. The verdict was: not sufficiently serious and responsible. A Professor Riem wrote in the highly respected scientific journal *Umschau*: ". . . At an altitude of only six to twelve miles the air is so rarefied that it is unable to offer any significant resistance to the exhaust gases. This means that these gases are ejected without any effect."

An officer who was in charge of an experimental rocket station commented as follows: "Experience has shown that rockets, even if they are fired from guns, cannot fly higher than three miles. In view of the well-known Prussian thoroughness, this is more or less the most that can be achieved." Professor Rudolf Franke of the Berlin Technical University, who was asked for a report, declared: "Although the calculations as such are correct, they must be based on *false* premises." This professor failed to reply to a letter from Oberth, asking him to explain what these false premises were.

Privy Councillor Spies disposes of Oberth's work in the *Zeitschrift für den mathematischen und physikalischen Unterricht* (Journal for Mathematics and Physics Teaching) in four lines which conclude with the following statement: ". . . but we believe that the time has not yet come to deal with such problems and will probably *never* come either."

The above is only a small selection from a large number of blunders presented in the form of expert opinion.

In spite of jealous critics, Oberth's book had created a stir all over the world. Only then people began to remember the older pioneers, and only then the names of Tsiolkovski, Goddard and others became more widely known. Development could no longer be held back, interest had been awakened and further progress became only a question of money.

On May 23, 1928 the motor manufacturer Fritz von Opel, driving the rocket-propelled car "Opel Rak II," fitted with twenty-four powder rockets, reached a speed of 143 miles per hour on the Avus Race Circuit in Berlin. The idea came from Max Valier, a Tyrolean born in Bozen, who was an enthusiastic pioneer of practical rocket-propulsion systems inspired by Oberth's ideas. It was a great sensation and amazement was worldwide. Although Opel was primarily interested in effective publicity for his cars, this experiment nevertheless provided proof of the suitability of rockets as means of propulsion. Max Valier branched out on his own. He built rocket sleds and shortly afterwards "Valier Rak Bob 2" reached a record speed of 248 miles per hour on Lake Starnberger. However, the passenger was only a sandbag. Valier, too, was not satisfied with solid-fuel rockets; he began, completely independently of Professor Goddard, to experiment with liquid propellants, developed a propulsion unit and on April 17, 1930, he was the first man to drive the rocket car "Rak 7" at the factory site of the firm of Heylandt in Berlin. This was true pioneering spirit because his liquid fuel propulsion unit was anything but safe in operation. Exactly one month later an explosion occurred during work on the test bench, in which Max Valier lost his life. He was the first victim of modern rocket engineering.

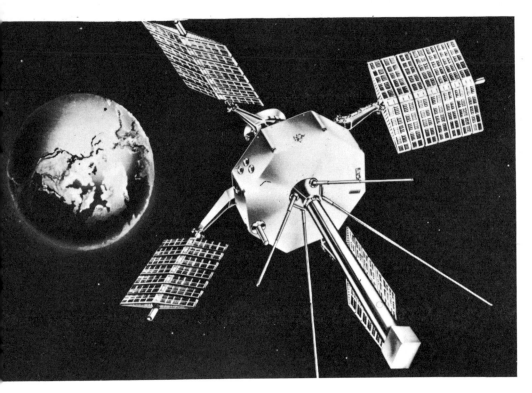

The Explorer XIV satellite launched on October 2, 1962 was designed to explore "weather in space."

Another pioneer of space travel must be remembered: the Austrian Guido von Pirquet (1880–1966) who published as early as 1928 in the journal *Die Rakete* (The Rocket) a work about interplanetary routes. The contents of this article were of far-reaching significance as far as space travel is concerned. The Russian space probe "Venusnik," launched on February 12, 1961, travelled very near the optimum path calculated in those early days by Pirquet. In addition, Pirquet showed in this work that while a direct flight from earth to the moon or the nearby planets is not possible, they can be reached if the spaceship is launched from a manned satellite, referred to as an outer-space station. The flight from such an outer-space station to the planets is easier to accomplish than the establishment of a station orbiting only a few hundred miles above earth. This fact was described by Pirquet as the "Cosmonautical Paradox" and has become an established concept in the terminology of space travel.

All that followed was the start of orderly development, the efforts of individuals were taken over by programs of entire organizations.

The Age of Space Travel Begins

October 3, 1942 was significant for space travel. For the first time in the history of rocket engineering, a large rocket with liquid propellants was successfully launched on that day. Anything that happened before can be described only as a series of more or less successful model tests.

But here, at the Peenemünde Experimental Station on the Baltic coast, the age of space travel was ushered in. A prominent eyewitness, General Walter Dornberger, the officer in charge of the Army Experimental Station, wrote an interesting report about those vital minutes:

A smoke cartridge hissed into the sky.

Its green trail near Test Stand VII drifted away sluggishly before the wind. Ten more seconds to go!

The picture on the television screen was unchanged.

"Ignition!"

The propulsion engineer must have pulled the first of the three main levers. I can see on the screen that clouds were issuing from the nozzle mouth. These were mingled with showers of sparks bouncing off the blast deflectors, scattering along the concrete platform on which stood the firing table.

"Preliminary!"

The shower of sparks quickly intensified into a flame and within a second changed into a fiery jet of a beautiful reddish yellow. The flame of the 8-ton thrust stage increased. The power developed by this preliminary stage was not yet sufficient to lift the 13·5-ton rocket from the firing table. Combustion of this stage lasted for three seconds. Smoke began to darken the picture. Cable ends, pieces of wood and chunks of turf flew through the air. I saw the casting-off cable detach itself from the rocket and fall downward. At the same moment the rocket was switched over to its own internal batteries.

27

The guiding mechanism now began to receive current from its own source.

"Cleared!"

The propulsion engineer had pulled the third and last main lever. Release of the casting-off cable meant that the principal stage was started. A turbo-pump operating at a speed of 4,000 revolutions per minute and with an output of more than 540 hp, started working, forcing $27\frac{1}{2}$ gallons of alcohol and oxygen per second into the combustion chamber of the rocket at a pressure of 43 pounds per square inch.

After about one second, the thrust reached 25 tons. With an acceleration similar to that of a falling stone the rocket climbed straight and steadily from the firing table and disappeared from the television screen, leaving behind it an immense, whirling cloud of dust.

Although this first giant rocket driven by liquid propellants was born under the sign of World War II, its designers had recognized with great foresight its true significance, extending far beyond the cruel day-to-day events. To mark the occasion which had at long last brought the long-hoped-for success, after many years of work frequently threatened by numerous setbacks, Dr. Dornberger arranged a small celebration for his closest colleagues in the evening of that memorable day in October, 1942. A speech given by Dornberger culminated in this important statement:

> . . . the following points may be deemed of decisive significance in the history of technology: we have invaded space with our rocket and for the first time—history, will record this, too—have used space as a bridge between two points on the earth; we have proved rocket propulsion practicable for space travel. To land, sea and air may now be added infinite space as a medium of future intercontinental traffic. This third day of October, 1942 is the beginning of a new era in transportation, that of space travel. . . .

What was the early history of this first large-scale liquid-propellant rocket, with the wartime name of V2 ("Vergeltungswaffe 2"="Retribution Weapon 2") but known to its creators by the more sober name of

A4 ("Aggregat 4" = "Unit 4"). The basic design of the A4 is based on Oberth's proposals. However, nineteen eventful years had passed between Oberth's first publication and the successful launching of an A4. A group of rocket enthusiasts, mainly young people, had in 1930 converted an old rifle range in Berlin-Reinickendorf into a rocket field where the would-be conquerors of space carried out their first practical experiments. Practical work was indeed necessary because since the time of the powder rockets, quite useful for pyrotechnics and sea-rescue purposes, rocket engineering had not made any further progress. The would-be conquerors of space had entered a completely unexplored field of engineering. They built "Miraks" and "Repulsors," and there were misfires, explosions, constant financial difficulties, but the enthusiasts were undaunted.

Gradually, the liquid-propellant rocket became reliable; there were flights to altitudes of up to 4,500 feet; the rocket men thought they had already conquered space by these flights. The fuel they used in their rockets consisted of 60–70 per cent. proof alcohol diluted with water and liquid oxygen. However, the most effective fuel was their enthusiasm and their selfless idealism. Nevertheless, by their own initiative and financial means, and without generous support from higher authorities, these rocket pioneers would never have been able to "build a spaceship." The days were past when an individual inventor or engineer, no matter how ingenious, or a private group of individuals would have been able to see through to its conclusion such a development project, in other words, to the stage of actual space travel.

In Germany the private groups were dissolved. Wernher von Braun, who in his student days had joined the group of enthusiastic Germans who were experimenting with rockets in Berlin–Reinickendorf had distinguished himself there by his great abilities. When the German Army took over the program von Braun was assigned to the experimental station of the Army Ordnance Office in Kummersdorf where the first scientifically equipped German test bench for liquid-propellant rockets was placed at his disposal. He began with his practical work on October 1, 1932; at the same time he continued his studies and obtained his doctorate at Berlin University with a thesis about theoretical and experimental contributions to the problem of the liquid-propellant rocket. Dr. Wernher von Braun, who was later awarded the title of Professor,

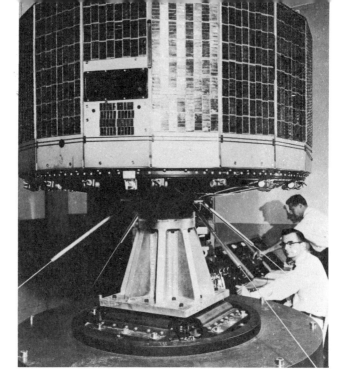

Right: Launch of a Vanguard rocket from Cape Canaveral.

Top left: A weather satellite is subjected to rigorous vibration tests before starting its journey around the world.

Bottom left: Tiros II, a weather satellite mounted on top of the booster rocket.

thus participated from the very start in the development of the modern rocket to which he contributed a great deal. At the beginning of 1936, the first sod was turned for the construction of the Peenemünde Army Experimental Station on the Baltic island of Usedom. Up to its destruction at the end of World War II, Peenemünde was the Mecca of rocket men. Not unlike Mecca, it was also a "forbidden city" to which only selected men were admitted.

Shortly before and during the first years of World War II, the units culminating in the A4 were developed. A1 was the first complete experimental rocket produced by the Kummersdorf Rocket Research Establishment. It weighed 330 pounds, had a length of 55 inches and a diameter of 12 inches. The combustion chamber produced a thrust of 660 pounds and burned 88 pounds of liquid propellants. However, the gyro fitted for stabilizing the rocket was mounted too far forward so that the rocket became nose-heavy. It was therefore unfit for flight and was not launched. But work continued undeterred and A1 was followed by A2, an improved design, launched successfully in 1934 from the Baltic island of Borkum, reaching an altitude of 7,200 feet. Unit 3 weighed 1,650 pounds and was 21 feet long; the tanks had a capacity of 990 pounds of liquid propellants, the combustion chambers with an improved cooling system delivered a thrust of 3,300 pounds for a period of 45 seconds. This model, too, was dogged by bad luck. In November, 1937, two designs were tested near an island called Greifswalder Oie but the control mechanism proved inadequate with the result that the rockets rose only a few hundred feet, then toppled and finally crashed into the sea.

At that time work was already in progress on the giant A4 rocket, whose first design dates from 1936. The actual development stage occupied three years. The first attempted launch on June 13, 1942 was a failure and so was the second one on August 16. Only the third attempt was completely successful: the rocket covered a distance of 120 miles.

Here are some of the most important details of the world's first big rocket:
Length 47 feet.
Launching weight 27,000 pounds.

Weight of propellants (liquid oxygen and alcohol) 8·8 tons.
Fuel: 75 per cent. ethyl alcohol and 25 per cent. water.
Pay-load 1,005 tons.
Length of rocket motor 68 inches.
Weight of combustion chamber 2,052 pounds.
Propellant consumption 276 pounds/s.
Maximum life of rocket engine 68 seconds.
Propellant flow rate 6,560 feet/s.
Temperature in the combustion chamber approximately 2,000° C.
Pressure in the combustion chamber 213 pounds/in.^{2}
Thrust at sea level 27 tons, at an altitude of 25 miles 32 tons.
Maximum acceleration 6 g.
Maximum speed 5,580 feet/s.
Maximum altitude after vertical climb: 132 miles.

During World War II, no fewer than 4,320 V2 rockets were launched for military purposes between September 6, 1944 and March 27, 1945, of which 1,120 were directed against London. With the end of the war, the military career of the A4 came to an end and it began a new, spectacular career in the service of science.

Between the earth's surface and outer space there is a blanket of air which plays a very important part in space travel because every space vehicle launched from earth must penetrate the atmosphere before reaching space, where there is virtually no air. Accurate knowledge of the atmosphere, its composition, extent, physical properties and air currents was and still is of the greatest importance to space travel. The V2, its military service over, represented a valuable research tool since even during the war a peak altitude of 107 miles, a world record, had been reached after a high-trajectory launch.

At the end of the war, the Americans still found parts of A4 rockets, among them 215 combustion chambers, and 200 turbo-pumps. These, together with 120 German experts, among them Professor Wernher von Braun, were shipped to the U.S.A. There, in the New Mexican desert, a new rocket test establishment already existed known as White Sands Proving Ground. It is picturesquely situated at the foot of a rocky range of the Organ Mountains which form part of the San Andres Range. At the other side, and parallel with it, rises the range of the Sacramento

Mountains and above them stretches the deep-blue and usually cloud-less sky of New Mexico. In that lonely part of the country the first steps were taken toward the exploration of the threshold of space.

There was great excitement at the proving ground on April 16, 1946. The first vertical launch of one of the prepared A4 rockets was imminent. Everything went according to plan but after the slim body of the rocket had risen, first slowly, then with increasing speed and accom-panied by the roar of the engines, riding on a jet of flame toward the cloudless sky, a fin came off after nineteen seconds and the engine had to be stopped by a radio signal. The pumps stopped working, the pro-pellant flow ceased and the rocket continued to rise only by its own inertia. Its speed dropped by thirty feet per second, then it turned and fell back to earth. Although the White Sands Proving Ground is large, being 100 miles long and twenty-eight miles wide, there was a risk of the rocket crashing beyond its limits, since A4 rockets have a range of 190 miles. The emergency cutout command had therefore to be given early enough to make sure that the rocket would crash within the prov-ing ground.

On one occasion, an A4 managed to escape in spite of most careful observation. The rocket had started properly and there were only a few seconds to go before burnout. At that moment, to the horror of the observers, the monster heeled over and started travelling along a southerly course, toward the Mexican border town of Ciudad Juarez. There were some tense moments before the message was received with great relief that the rocket had crashed one mile outside the town with-out causing any damage. When crashing, a large rocket, even without explosive charge, develops a terrific destructive force. The blockhouses at the rocket launching sites have nine-foot-thick walls, the roof is up to twenty-five feet thick and even the floor is made of ten-foot-thick reinforced concrete. A4 rockets crashing into the desert have dug craters of up to sixty-five feet in depth. On May 10, 1946, the first successful high-altitude flight in the service of science took place. The A4 rocket reached an altitude of seventy miles and returned after seven minutes, crashing at a distance of thirty-one miles from the launching site.

As soon as the point of impact is reported to the Launch Command Center, a recovery team sets out and the fragments are carefully col-lected for detailed examination.

Within those few minutes of a flight, the rocket has to perform important tasks. On February 20, 1947, an A4 rocket was launched for the first time with scientific instruments and tiny living creatures on board. The first rocket passengers to undertake a flight up to the threshold of space were fruitflies (drosophilia.) The instrument capsule, a cylindrical body twenty-nine inches long with a diameter of fourteen inches, returned to earth by parachute and landed undamaged. Whereas the rocket flight lasted only six minutes, the instrument capsule attached to the ribbon-type parachute travelled for a total of forty-four minutes. For the first time photographs were taken of earth from space. Altogether sixty-nine A4 rockets were launched, sixty-six of these at White Sands. A total of twenty tons of instruments was lifted during these flights.

In this way, the first important preparatory work for space travel was carried out. However, an A4 rocket was far from being a spaceship because the power developed by its motors was not yet sufficient to completely overcome the attraction of earth. The first and really serious enemy which rocket engineers had to defeat in order to get their machines away from earth, was and is gravity. All bodies, whether living or lifeless matter, are subject to gravity and there are no means of eliminating gravity; all that can be done is to overcome it by an opposing force.

The achievement of space travel is based on a few very simple, easily understood considerations. If we lift a stone in opposition to gravity, the opposing force is provided by our muscles. But here something very important must be added. For instance, if we lift a cobblestone we have to press very hard against the ground with our feet, in other words, we need something against which to push. To overcome gravity on the earth's surface such support is essential, for example a crane lifting heavy loads on a building site. Even a balloon rising into the air is supported by something: the air provides buoyancy; in the case of a surfacing submarine, it is the buoyancy of the water which causes the submarine to rise. In the case of propeller-driven and jet aircraft, it is the air which helps to carry the weight (wings.) This is why an aircraft of this type can climb only as high as the extent of the layer of air capable of supporting it. The limit for balloons lies at an altitude of approximately twenty-five miles.

What supports a missile when it leaves not only the earth's surface but even the earth's atmosphere? Jules Verne had his space travellers fly inside a projectile fired from a gun. In principle, this would be possible but in practice it would not work. In the first place, the pressure due to acceleration during launching would crush the passengers and secondly the air resistance would present an insurmountable obstacle. If the earth had no atmosphere, it would be possible to hit the moon with a projectile fired from a gun giving the projectile a speed of approximately 6·8 miles per second.

This is a very important piece of information. There is a velocity at which a body travelling from an "ideal" earth surface (without atmosphere) would no longer fall back to earth. This velocity, in the case of earth approximately seven miles per second, is aptly referred to as escape velocity, and is also called the Second Cosmic Velocity. Sometimes the expression parabolic velocity is used because a projectile fired at this velocity, and not in a vertical direction, would leave the earth on a parabolic trajectory. A stone dropping from a stationary position from an infinite distance from earth would hit the earth's surface at the same velocity.

Let us carry out a second firing experiment on an "ideal" earth surface. To this end, however, it would be necessary for us to imagine the earth's surface as smooth as a billiard ball. We train the barrel of our gun to an exactly horizontal position and fire increasingly powerful charges from this "ideal gun." The more powerful the charge on each occasion, the farther the projectile will fly, or in other words, the more energy we apply on firing, the greater the distances we shall achieve. Ultimately we shall reach a charge at which the projectile will not hit the ground at all but will circle the earth. We have to be careful, though, to make sure that the projectile will not hit us from behind! It will then orbit round the "ideal earth" for ever, like the moon, but at a lower altitude. If we had measured the velocity of the projectile, we would have discovered that it was 4·9 miles per second. This is another very important discovery. There is a velocity at which a body accelerated horizontally, will follow a circular orbit; for that reason this velocity is also referred to as "orbital velocity" or First Cosmic Velocity.

Some people have difficulty in visualizing that a body within a few hundred miles' distance from the earth's surface, in other words, still almost within the range of undiminished gravity, does not crash to earth, although it is not "fastened" to anything. This latter concept is not quite correct; our projectile is "fastened" to an opposing force which, however, is invisible. We know that when we drive around a bend, a force occurs which tries to carry the vehicle outward; this force also causes skidding. It is the centrifugal force which becomes the greater, the tighter the bend and the higher the speed. In the case of our orbital velocity, the centrifugal force is exactly equal to the force of attraction of the earth. The artificial satellites circling the earth outside the effective atmosphere are, as it were, suspended by the centrifugal force. But as soon as their speed is reduced, the centrifugal force decreases and the earth's attraction gains the upper hand; the satellite keeps coming closer to earth and its ultimate crash is inevitable.

The orbital velocity depends on the altitude at which a satellite moves around the earth: the greater the height the lower the speed. The moon has an orbital velocity of only 3,280 feet per second.

The escape velocity also depends on the height of the launching site above sea level but it is customary to relate it to the surface of the planet.

Now we know the essential conditions for space travel: at least the first cosmic velocity must be reached to prevent the spaceship from falling back to earth, but this does not provide complete escape from our planet. These figures have been known for a long time but nobody dared hope that a man-made spacecraft would ever be able to attain such velocities because they require a huge amount of energy which appeared impossible to achieve. We can illustrate this by means of a simple example.

Let us assume we wish to lift a weight of one kilogram (2·2 pounds) from earth to a point at the distance of the moon. How great would be the effort required? It would be exactly the same as that required for lifting a load of 6,380 tons to a height of one meter (39 inches.) Many people were frightened off by this figure; only the unshakable optimists among the rocket pioneers did not give up. They introduced a new concept—the multistage principle. They reasoned quite correctly: should it prove impossible to reach orbital velocity with one rocket, it should be possible with two or three.

This was a solution that had occurred already to the early pioneers of the ideas of space travel. But often it is a very long way from an idea to its realization and so we must not be surprised that it was only on February 24, 1949 that a really successful two-stage rocket thundered skyward from the White Sands Proving Ground. The booster stage was the well-tried and successful A4 rocket, while the second stage consisted of a small high-altitude research rocket developed in the U.S.A. and given the name of WAC Corporal (WAC stands for Women's Army Corps). Individually, the A4 would have reached an altitude of not more than 100 or 120 miles and the WAC Corporal only forty-three miles. When the launch took place on February 14, 1949, the rocket experts dared only to hope faintly that on this occasion the rocket would push its nose into space. The powerful A4 rocket, weighing over 12 tons, was fitted at its nose with the slim WAC Corporal weighing slightly less than 660 pounds. The second stage was, as it were, placed on a flying launching pad which one minute after launching had already reached an altitude of nineteen miles and a speed of 2,600 miles per hour. At that moment, the two stages separated, the WAC Corporal was ignited and accelerated further by its own power whereas the first stage continued only by its own inertia, reaching an altitude of sixty-three miles. The A4 then dropped back and crashed into the desert. In the meantime, the WAC Corporal continued its flight, reaching a speed of 5,160 miles per hour when the motor cut out. With this tremendous momentum it continued to rise higher and higher, up to the very edge of space, much higher than any man-made object had ever travelled away from the surface of the earth. The rocket continued to climb until it had reached an altitude of slightly more than 250 miles, then it stopped and the free fall back to earth began. Gravity had still won this time, but the multistage principle had proved its usefulness and had shown the way to the stars. The WAC Corporal crashed into the desert twelve minutes after· launching, eighty miles away from the launching pad. This high-altitude record was not broken for many years, at least as far as official statements are concerned. In those days it was merely a question of time as to when space travel would become reality. The basic conditions had been created, rocket engineering had made tremendous progress and governmental interest in space travel had been aroused. And yet the optimists did not dare to make any definite prophecies as to when the first artificial satellite would be circling the earth.

Right: Echo II undergoing inspection.

In the meantime, work proceeded on the high-altitude research rockets. The Americans developed the "Viking." By comparison with the A4, it incorporated many improvements and was able to exceed considerably the high-altitude record of the A4. This rocket also made it possible to lift various measuring instruments to high altitudes. The most successful Viking rocket was launched from the White Sands Proving Ground on May 14, 1954. It reached an altitude of 160 miles, successfully carrying out measurements of cosmic radiation and taking photographs of Earth. This high-altitude record also demonstrated the performance limits of single-stage rockets using conventional chemical propellants. For a better understanding of this achievement let us look at the most important data of Viking II which made this record flight:

Peak altitude	159 miles
Life of rocket engine	103 seconds
Duration of flight	557 seconds
Speed at burnout	6,300 feet per second
Thrust	21,380 lbf
Pay load	830 pounds
Oxygen	55,820 pounds
Alcohol	5,750 pounds
Peroxide	385 pounds
Total propellants	11,570 pounds
Design weight	2,200 pounds
Weight at launch	14,990 pounds
Length	42 feet
Diameter	3 feet 9 inches

During the year of the successful record flight of a Viking rocket there took place in Rome from September 30 to October 4 a meeting of a special committee to prepare for the International Geophysical Year. On that occasion the idea of using artificial satellites in the uppermost atmosphere as means of research, was seriously considered. Space travel had thus become "respectable" from a scientific point of view also, even if many conservative scientists did not think much of such "innovations." The Americans were, nevertheless, busy with a satellite project

The Syncom communication satellite has a height of 25 inches. Sunlight is converted into electric current by 3,960 silicone cells mounted on the side walls.

which was given the name "Vanguard" and a newspaper published in Moscow announced, on April 15, 1955, that the Academy of Science of the U.S.S.R. was also working on a satellite project.

Official confirmation followed soon afterward. On July 29, President Eisenhower's press secretary announced: "I declare in the name of the President that he has approved our country's plans concerning the launching of small, unmanned earth satellites. These are to represent

41

the contribution of the United States to the International Geophysical Year. . . ."

The Russian delegate, Professor Leonid Sedov confirmed at the Sixth International Astronautical Congress in Copenhagen during the same year that the Soviet Union would also be launching satellites during the International Geophysical Year. Thus, the blueprints for the decisive chapter in space travel were prepared.

Trail-blazers in Space

And yet, the whole world was surprised by a sensational news report on October 4, 1957, *the* sensation of the year:

The Soviet Union had succeeded in orbiting an artificial satellite around the earth. The Russian word *"sputnik"* (meaning satellite) had suddenly become a new term in all languages. The accurate scientific description of Sputnik I was: *Iskustvennye Sputnik Semliy* or artificial earth satellite. The world public was surprised about several facts. Firstly, that it was the Russians who had won the race and that the satellite circling the earth was not a Vanguard although it had appeared that the Americans, with their high altitude research rockets and their team of experts around Wernher von Braun, were in the lead. The second surprise was the considerable weight of Sputnik I which, with its weight of 184 pounds was approximately eight times as heavy as the planned Vanguard satellite. People craned their necks, just as they did in grandfather's day when a flying machine hummed across the sky, to see the dot of light which would, within a few minutes, travel as an artificial star in the opposite direction to the sun and moon. Finally, experts were amazed at the accuracy with which the multistage booster rocket had placed Sputnik into orbit. Its perigee, that is to say the point of its trajectory nearest the earth, was 145 miles, and its apogee, that farthest from the earth, 588 miles. Inside the spherical 22·8-inch diameter satellite were fitted two transmitters broadcasting signals on wavelengths of 7·5 metres and 15 metres which were received as bleeps. Sputnik raced around the earth every 96·2 minutes.

All doubts were now dispelled. Engineering science had reached a point enabling it to despatch artificial satellites into space, unmanned vehicles which, equipped with scientific instruments, would be able to explore the cosmic vicinity of our planet. They can thus be regarded as trail-blazers probing the path leading to manned space flight, thereby performing most valuable pioneer work.

On November 3, 1957, barely one month later, the whole world was amazed to find that Sputnik I was followed by the launching of a second artificial satellite, Sputnik II. This could be regarded as a proper miniature spaceship because with its weight of 1,120 pounds it was able to carry a passenger into orbit. The passenger was the now famous dog, Laika, the first living creature from our earth to circle our planet in a satellite orbit and so live permanently in a condition of weightlessness. The orbit of Sputnik II approached the earth at its nearest point at an altitude of 150 miles, but the point farthest from the earth was 1,056 miles; this is the reason for its longer orbital period by comparison with Sputnik I. Sputnik II took 103 minutes to circle the earth.

Laika's fate was tragic because it was impossible to bring Sputnik II back to earth. In those days re-entry techniques had not been sufficiently developed and after one week it was no longer possible to maintain life-supporting conditions. Laika became a martyr to space science. The tremendous value of her feat was that she proved that manned space flights were possible. Man is capable of creating artificial life-supporting conditions and to control launching in such a manner that higher organisms do not suffer damage in the process.

The ascents of the high-altitude research rockets had provided an important piece of knowledge. The earth's atmosphere extends much farther than had previously been assumed. This was also confirmed by the first two Sputniks. Their perigees just about touched the effective atmosphere and the resulting friction slowed them down, leading finally to their burnup. Sputnik I burned up on January 4, 1958 and Sputnik II on April 13 of the same year. Their orbital life amounted only to a few months.

On January 31, 1958, the Americans, too, succeeded in launching a satellite. Basically it was an improvised launch. Originally, Project Vanguard had been planned, but up to that point it had not shown any success. Here, Professor Wernher von Braun came to the rescue. He and his team possessed all the experience necessary for the successful launching of a booster rocket. The simpler and the more proven a design, the fewer trouble·sources there are.

It was left to von Braun to increase the prestige of American rocket research. He did not become involved in any experiments but simply chose for the first stage of his booster rocket a military rocket called

Redstone. This was nothing but an improved version of the old A4 rocket. He built up the other three stages from solid-propellant rockets offering the advantage of great reliability. The whole vehicle was named Jupiter-C, the mysterious, "C" meaning "composed." The second stage consisted of a cluster of eleven solid-propellant rockets (each fifty inches in diameter); the third stage consisted only of three solid-propellant rockets of the same type, arranged concentrically within the second stage. The fourth and final stage consisted simply of a single solid-propellant rocket, also of the same type (its name was Recruit,) which was rigidly connected to the cylindrical satellite casing and together with the satellite had a length of eighty inches. All the upper stages were spun at high speed before launching so that they acted like a gyro and therefore maintained the position of their axis in space. This is called spin stabilization. The first artificial American satellite was thus placed in orbit by a four-stage rocket. Accurate records exist of this historic event and they convey the tension and excitement accompanying a satellite launching, even today.

Let us relive those minutes at Cape Canaveral, now called Cape Kennedy.

22.47 hours 30 seconds: Moser starts the countdown: "X minus 30 ... X minus 20 ... X minus 10 – 9 – 8 – 7 – 6 – 5 – 4 – 3 – 2 – 1 – firing command!"

X plus 3 seconds. The propellant tanks of the first stage, the Redstone, are pressurized.

X plus 11 seconds. The last plug-in connection is severed.

X plus 12 seconds. Ignition. An orange ball of fire becomes visible, thrust is building up. "Go Baby!" somebody calls out in the control bunker. "Baby" weighed forty-five tons! From the outside a tremendous roar sounding like an earthquake penetrates into the blockhouse.

X plus 16. Lift-off! The whole launching pad is covered by a cloud from which the Jupiter-C rocket rises majestically, at first slowly, and then climbs toward the sky with increasing speed.

General Medaris and Dr. Debus rush to the DOVAP (Doppler Velocity and Position Instrument) which measures the speed of the climbing rocket with the aid of radio waves employing the Doppler effect. The recording pens draw their graphs along the paper. Suddenly they are sharply deflected toward the left—the booster rocket has entered the zone of high-altitude storms, then the pens return and the rocket is free. During the following forty seconds the tension becomes almost unbearable and it looks as if the launching would end in failure. The speed of the rocket is also presented in the form of an audio signal. This signal suddenly fades out with a whimper, and there is a deathly silence in the command centre.

"I've lost my signal!" Medaris shouts into the telephone connecting him with the assembly hall of the Redstone where the missile test director and his men are at work. The disappearance of the speed signal usually means the beginning of the end. A murmur of disappointment runs through in the command center. A young Jupiter Project officer telephones the central instrumentation station: "Lost signal in the command center, what is your signal like?"

"Noisy, but acceptable!"

A sigh of relief can be heard at the command center. The "workhorse" of space travel, as Redstone has been called, has once again worked well. One hundred and fifty seconds after launching, burnout takes place at an altitude of sixty-two miles and the Redstone rocket separates; its forward part, the three upper stages, still remain together as a complete unit. Gradually this part is reorientated into a horizontal line and with the aid of compressed-air nozzles it is aligned with the utmost care parallel with the surface of the earth. This is done with an accuracy of a tenth of a degree, because if the error is more than two or three degrees, the missile will again enter into denser layers of air and will not complete even a single orbit. The upper stages spin at a speed of 760 revolutions per minute.

The most important task during launching is the accurate prediction of the peak altitude. This is the job of Dr. Ernst Stuhlinger, one of Professor Wernher von Braun's closest collaborators. The moment at which the rocket reaches the highest point of its trajectory is determined simultaneously by means of several methods from the ascent data, among them Doppler and radar. After 260 seconds following cutout the zenith of the trajectory is reached according to the mean value obtained from different test results. The moment has arrived; Dr. Stuhlinger presses a button and a cluster of eleven solid-propellant rockets is ignited by remote control.

Everything else happens within seconds. After approximately six seconds the second stage is burned out, the third and then the fourth stages are ignited. The final-stage rocket accelerates the satellite to a speed of 18,330 miles per hour. Seven minutes have passed since the launch: Explorer I, that is the name given to the satellite, has reached its earth orbit. At that moment nobody knows what the elliptic trajectory of the satellite will look like. Professor Wernher von Braun and Dr. William H. Pickering are far away in Washington and are understandably excited. The preliminary orbital calculation has shown that Explorer I should appear above San Diego, California, after 106 minutes. This means almost two hours of uncertainty.

After 106 minutes, San Diego reports: "We can't hear anything!"

Von Braun and Pickering once again check the calculated timetable of Explorer I. Von Braun says: "The thing must have flown farther out into space than planned."

Pickering yells into the telephone to one of his colleagues in San Diego: "Frank, why the devil don't you hear anything?"

But another eight seemingly endless minutes passed. As von Braun and Dr. Stuhlinger, among others, said later to the author of this book, those were the most exciting minutes of their lives. Just as all hope began to fade, San Diego came on the line and Pickering, who took the call, shouted jubilantly: "He's there. We've got him!"

At that time, Explorer I had almost completed its first orbit and is still circling the earth. It circles our planet once every 100 minutes. Its pronounced elliptical track approaches the earth's surface to a distance of approximately 210 miles; the maximum distance between Explorer I and earth is approximately 930 miles.

The tiny artificial moon, created by man and with a payload of only eighteen pounds, has on board test instruments and radio transmitters; the latter have, however, fallen silent long ago. But as long as they broadcast their coded signals, they transmitted valuable information to earth, amongst other data about radiation conditions outside the atmosphere of our planet. The American physicist Dr. James A. van Allen, who processed the test results, made a very important discovery.

Earth is surrounded by a belt of extremely intensive radiation, commencing at an altitude of approximately 320 miles and extending far into space, approximately up to six or seven earth radii. The maximum

47

of the radiation intensity is 10,000 times stronger than normally encountered in space, say, for example, between earth and moon.

The earth's magnetic field has the ability to store electrically-charged radiation particles for a considerable period of time. Thus a belt is formed, similar to a car tire, lying in the plane of the magnetic equator around our planet. This belt is full of protons, electrons and other elementary particles. In the case of protons and electrons we talk about corpuscular radiation, in the case of ultraviolet and X rays we talk about wave radiation. The corpuscular radiation originated partly from the depth of space (cosmic radiation) or from the sun. Those originating from the sun play an important part in manned space flight, but more about this later.

This radiation belt surrounding the earth was called the van Allen belt after its discoverer and represented a great surprise for geo-physicists, because prior to the flight of Explorer I nobody had the faintest idea of the presence of such a zone of radiation around the earth. If a spaceship leaves the earth in the direction of the equatorial plane, it has to cross the van Allen belt, but in the direction of the poles, a radiation-free trajectory is possible.

The start of the first artificial satellite marked the beginning of the age of space travel. In the meantime, things have livened up around our earth. If we were able to observe our planet from a vantage point a few thousand miles out in space, and if our eyesight were extremely good, we would notice that more than a hundred tiny moons are circling the earth, mostly in very low orbits. An attentive extra-terrestrial observer would also have noticed that some of these moons were visible for only a few hours, days, weeks and months, and then disappeared without trace. Those were the satellites which either because of their low perigee were short-lived or were successfully brought back to earth.

Artificial satellites have to perform a large variety of scientific and engineering tasks. That is the explanation for the variety of their appearance and equipment. All active satellites are fitted with a transmitter which in turn requires a power source (battery.) The first satellites were fitted with batteries whose working life was limited. When the battery is exhausted, the satellite falls silent and is then described as a dead satellite. But there are unlimited amounts of solar energy available in space. No cloud ever hides the sun and it was, therefore, decided at an

Telstar I, the television satellite during assembly. The dark areas are the solar batteries supplying electric power for the instruments. The two equatorial belts are the transmitting and receiving aerials.

early stage to utilize this inexhaustible source of energy to operate the equipment and transmitters carried by the artificial satellite. This is why solar batteries were developed. These are based on the ability of some materials to convert light directly into electrical current. As a rule, a large number of silicon cells are used for this purpose. The first artificial satellite fitted with such solar batteries is Vanguard I, weighing only $3\frac{1}{4}$ pounds, launched on March 17, 1958 from Cape Canaveral. It will probably keep circling the earth for another 200 years. Its perigee of 409 miles is comparatively high and its apogee takes it to a distance of 2,450 miles from the earth. The period of one orbit was calculated as 134 minutes. With the aid of this satellite it was possible to determine accurately the shape of the earth and it appears that the pressure of solar radiation also influences the track of this satellite. In the distant future, Vanguard I will become a kind of cosmic museum piece, because whereas in about 100 years' time most of the artificial satellites of the early days will have burned out in the earth's atmosphere, Vanguard will be one of the last survivors of its time. The solar cells still functioned perfectly for seven years after its launching; Vanguard I fell silent only in the Spring of 1965.

Among the long list of tiny man-made moons circling our earth, only a few of the most prominent ones of the early days will be mentioned.

On May 15, 1958 the Soviet Union launched Sputnik III. It caused a sensation because of its weight (2,919 pounds.)

Its orbit brings it to within 140 miles of the earth's surface and at its farthest point it is 1,168 miles away. The original period was 106 minutes but became shorter toward the end of its comparatively long life, because Sputnik III dropped back into denser layers of air, where it burned out on April 6, 1960, after almost eleven months in orbit. This is the fate of all artificial satellites whose orbit does not take them far enough away from the fatal embrace of the atmosphere surrounding our planet. The friction of the air, which is extremely rarefied at the altitudes of most satellite tracks, leads sooner or later to a shrinkage of the orbit in a rather peculiar manner. A satellite is subjected to the strongest air resistance at its perigee. The resulting minute reduction in speed has the effect that the apogee, the point farthest away from the earth, approaches closer and closer with each orbit while the perigee remains almost unchanged. The result is that the shape of the orbit becomes more and more like a circle until finally a circular orbit is reached at the altitude of the perigee. At that time, however, disaster is imminent. The orbit begins to shrink rapidly, the artificial satellite becomes a meteor which burns out at an altitude of between thirty and sixty miles. This is the fate suffered by a large proportion of all artificial satellites launched so far.

The satellite which will be described now had a very short life. However, within this short life it achieved a unique and novel feat. On December 18, 1958 the Americans launched "Project Score," whose name is made up from the words Satellite Communication Orbital Relay Experiment. An Atlas-type booster rocket propelled itself into space to act as a satellite. Its launch weight was more than 110 tons, and since this rocket only jettisons the rocket engines, it cannot really be described as a proper multistage rocket. It is thus able to carry itself into orbit with an orbital weight of four tons, but at the expense of the payload which must not exceed 220 pounds. This satellite was fitted with a tape recorder and radio transmitting and receiving equipment. By means of special control circuits it was possible to interrogate the satellite and

On October 29, 1961 the chimpanzee Enos orbited the earth twice in a Mercury capsule.

make it play back the stored messages. The communication experiment was successful beyond expectation. The most famous part of it was the Christmas speech by the then American President Eisenhower which was transmitted by the Atlas-Score satellite. Speech and conversations were capable of being transmitted from ground stations to the satellite where they were stored and played back on command. This was the first time in the history of space flight technology that a human voice could be heard via space.

On August 7, 1959 the Americans launched the first paddle-wheel satellite, Explorer VI. The solar batteries were mounted on extensions similar to the sails of a windmill to obtain more energy from a larger surface. This is why the Americans called it "paddle-wheel satellite." These extensions were deployed only after arrival in space. The four paddles were fitted on both sides with 1,000 silicone cells each. The weight of the satellite was 142 pounds and the nearly spherical spacecraft was able to perform fifteen scientific experiments. Due to the fact that its trajectory carried it to a distance of 26,400 miles from earth, the results it returned were most instructive. This satellite discovered a ring current of electrons around the earth, enabled a more detailed map of the van Allen belt to be drawn and broadcast to earth that the temperature inside the satellite fluctuated between $-3 \cdot 85°$ C and $+45 \cdot 65°$ C. Since its perigee was only 155 miles up, its life was only approximately two years.

The year 1959 did not produce any further spectacular achievements in the field of artificial satellites. It should be mentioned, however, that the Americans placed satellites into a polar orbit for the first time with the Discoverer series. Discover I was launched on February 28, 1959. Up to then all satellites, those launched by the Soviet Union as well as by the United States, were placed in orbits which in the case of the Russian satellites were inclined by more than 60° and in the case of the American satellites by more than 30° toward the equator. The polar orbit has an inclination of 90° relative to the equator, the satellite passes in one orbit over both poles and in due course also over all parts of the earth's surface since our planet continues to rotate while the satellite orbits above. Explorer I, whose orbit had an inclination of $33\frac{1}{3}°$ relative to the equator, only passes over a belt of the earth extending from latitudes $33\frac{1}{3}°$ North to $33\frac{1}{3}°$ South. The satellites of the Discoverer series (no fewer than eight were launched in 1959) also had the task of studying the problem of re-entry. For that reason, the capsule, from Discoverer II onwards, was provided with a separation device and means for braking. In the case of Discoverer VIII, launched on November 10, 1959, the return to earth took place according to plan, the beacon transmitter in the capsule functioned properly and was heard by the recovery aircraft, but neither aircraft nor ships were able to locate the capsule.

April 1, 1960 saw the launching of a memorable satellite. Up to that time all satellite flights were exclusively of scientific or engineering significance and one could hardly speak of any immediate practical value. With the launching of the first weather observation satellite, Tiros I, a new era in space flight had begun.

From earth or from an aircraft, only a small weather region can be observed at one time; over large areas, for example, the oceans, there are no weather stations at all. The closer the net of observation posts, the more accurate the weather forecasts will be. A satellite circling the earth at a great altitude and fitted with television cameras and transmitters is able to provide a very comprehensive picture of the general weather situation over a large part of the earth's surface. Tiros I (Television Infrared Observation Satellite) orbits the earth at a height of approximately 435 miles and completes one orbit every 99·2 minutes. The entire satellite weighs 275 pounds, is equipped with two television cameras of which one observes an area of 800 by 800 miles and the other an area of 80 by 80 miles. The pictures can be stored on magnetic tape and can be transmitted to earth on command. This radio picture installation operated for three months and of the nearly 23,000 pictures transmitted, 60 per cent. were usable. The pictures showed jet streams, storms and fronts. On April 10, 1960 it proved possible to observe at a distance of 800 miles east of Brisbane, Australia, the formation of a hurricane which had not been noticed by any other weather station. Tiros I was followed by other, further-improved weather satellites. On June 13, 1963, Tiros VII was launched from Cape Canaveral into an orbit with an altitude between 385 and 405 miles. With the aid of two wide-angle cameras, it transmitted picture of cloud formations to earth, performed infrared radiation measurements and carried an instrument on board for determining electron temperatures.

Tiros V, launched on June 19, 1962 and which ceased transmitting pictures after a working life of ten and a half months on May 4, 1963 during its 4,580th orbit, has a very proud record indeed. The number of pictures, totalling 58,226, represented in those days a record for the Tiros satellites. More than 80 per cent. of those pictures were found suitable for the purpose of weather forecasting. On the basis of transmitted pictures of cloud formations provided by Tiros V, the U.S. Weather Bureau was able to issue 396 gale warnings to numerous countries all over the world; these included early warnings of two hurricanes and four typhoons. As a result of such early warnings, made possible only by observations from space, many lives were saved and great damage was averted. This is one way in which artificial satellites have already proved their worth.

On August 12, 1960 a further important event was recorded in the history of satellites. The instrument capsule of Discoverer XIII, weighing 286 pounds, was recovered from the sea not far from Hawaii. That made it possible, for the first time, to locate an object brought down to earth from orbit. A few days later, a really exceptional feat was performed. The instrument capsule of Discoverer XIV was caught with a net and recovered on August 14 after its return from orbit by an aircraft flying at an altitude of 10,000 feet. These experiments must be considered as important preparations for manned satellite flight for which the successful solution of the re-entry problem was the essential precondition.

As early as May 15, 1960 the Russians had placed into orbit a very heavy satellite, Sputnik IV, weighing over four tons and carrying a payload of 3,260 pounds; an attempted return was, however, unsuccessful. The day after the successful catch of the instrument capsule of Discoverer XIV on August 20, 1960, the Russians also succeeded in solving the re-entry problem and in a most impressive manner, too. Sputnik V, launched on August 19, carried two dogs, Byelka and Strelka, as well as forty mice, all of whom returned safely to earth. This was a real spaceship, weighing 10,140 pounds. A further attempt in December of the same year failed, the drama of Sputnik II being repeated with Sputnik VI. The capsule launched on December 1 burned out after seventeen orbits, together with the two dogs on board.

In the meantime, the Americans were able to score another important success. The active telecommunications satellite Courier IB placed into orbit on October 4, 1960 by means of a Type Thor-Able-Star rocket, achieved technical feats bordering on the fabulous. More than 70 per cent. of the surface of the spherical satellite (diameter 51 inches, weight 50 pounds) is covered with a total of 19,152 solar cells for charging nickel-cadmium batteries fitted inside the satellite. The output of the photocells, totalling 64 W, is higher than that achieved by any earlier satellite. Data are stored on five magnetic tapes, four for teleprinter and facsimile radio transmission and one for voice radio. Signals were received and transmitted by four receivers and four transmitters. To that were added two command receivers, two telemetering transmitters and two radio location transmitters. This telecommunications satellite, whose active life is estimated at 200 years, was able to transmit 340,000 words within five minutes. All artificial satellites referred to so far were active communication satellites carrying test instruments and transmitters on board. On August 12, 1960, the Americans placed a passive communications satellite in orbit; a very interesting experiment, especially remarkable as an engineering feat which proved fully successful. The object was to test a passive reflector for radio signals in a satellite orbit. The most suitable design appeared to be a balloon which, however, could be inflated only after the satellite had entered into orbit. As the main task of this balloon was to reflect back radio waves, it was given the name of Echo I. It was one of the most remarkable phenomena in the night sky. It was the brightest star created and sent around the earth by man: its brilliance competed with that of the brightest objects in the sky, with the exception of the sun and moon. The launching of Echo I was a masterpiece of engineering on the part of the Americans. A three-stage Thor-Delta booster rocket with a launch weight of fifty tons carried the balloon satellite, folded up inside a small magnesium sphere weighing only twenty-four pounds, into a very high orbit, 860 miles above the earth's surface. It was possible to place Echo I into an almost circular orbit where it circled the earth once every two hours. After entering orbit, the balloon was automatically inflated and assumed the shape of a giant 100-foot diameter sphere. The actual balloon consists of a plastic skin of Mylar only 0·127 millimeters (0·005 inches) thick on which was deposited an aluminum layer of only two thousandths of a millimeter or 0·000078-inch thickness. These delicate layers of skin show

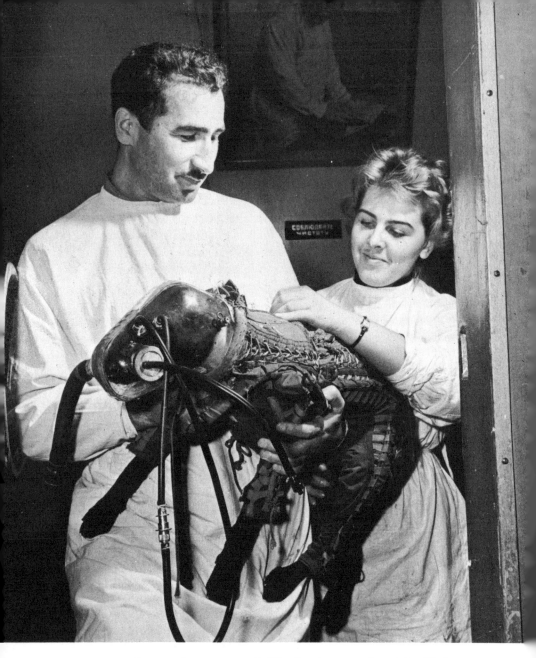

Dog wearing a spacesuit. The Russians experimented with dogs . . .

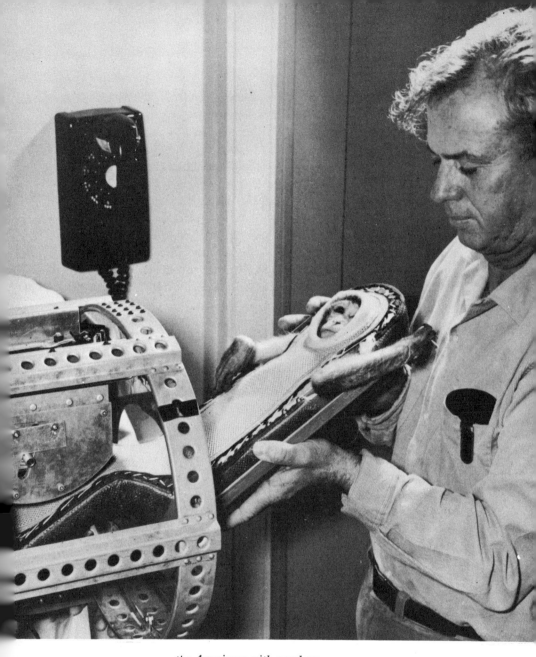

. . . the Americans with monkeys.

how the low weight of the balloon was achieved: the plastic skin weighs only 132 pounds and the aluminum layer only 4·4 pounds. Fitted at two opposite points on the equator of the sphere were two radiolocation transmitters each weighing only 11 ounces. The balloon was inflated to its full size by residues of air, 11 pounds of benzoic acid and 19 pounds of anthraquinone; these chemicals in powder form evaporated in the vacuum of space, thereby filling the envelope with gas. The internal pressure is, however, incredibly low and amounts to only a three-millionth part of atmospheric pressure at sea level. It was thought originally that Echo I would have a life of only about thirteen months. However, it proved surprisingly tough because even at the beginning of 1967 its appearance was still conspicuous. As a result of its large distance from earth, it traverses the sky comparatively slowly; it moves in opposition to the rotation of the earth, that is to say from right to left, and a change of position is noticeable within a few seconds. Because of its large size and very low mass, an extremely low density and even the radiation pressure due to the sun cause changes in its orbit. At an altitude of 930 miles the air density was found to amount to only one-trillionth gram per cubic centimeter. The last traces of the blanket of air surrounding our planet extend farther out into space that was assumed previously. Prior to 1957, that is, before artificial satellites were launched, such a density was thought to exist at an altitude of only 500 miles. The balloon satellite Echo I has also shown that the risk of meteorite impact is very low. Had the envelope of Echo I been pierced by meteorites during its almost eight years in orbit, it would have lost its gas charge a long time ago. It burned up in the earth's atmosphere in May, 1968 and was replaced by Echo II, launched on January 25, 1964 and shining even more brightly.

A further, but much smaller balloon satellite with a diameter of 140 inches was launched under the name of Explorer IX on February 16, 1961 for the purpose of measuring the density of air in space. On that occasion a solid-propellant rocket, a four-stage Scout was used as booster for the first time. The further development of artificial satellites shows two distinct features: first, their use for practical purposes—above all in the service of telecommunications—and secondly as preparation for manned space flights. For example, on March 25, 1961, the Russians launched a Sputnik-type space cabin weighing 4·7 tons, carrying animals mainly for the purpose of studying all processes during launch, flight and return with a view to manned space flights. The Americans were also working toward the same goal. On September 13, 1961 they carried out a test flight with a Mercury capsule of the type used later for manned flights. During that flight the capsule carried a robot, a dummy Astronaut in place of a man.

The year 1961 saw a great deal of activity as far as satellites were concerned. It is impossible to list all of them here but it is worth mentioning that on one occasion, for example, three satellites were launched by a single booster rocket, that a navigation satellite (to enable ships to fix their position) was fitted with an atomic battery, and that satellites were placed into orbit for measuring the effect of sunspots on radio communications. Moreover, satellites were launched for studying the Northern Lights, for measuring cosmic radiation and magnetic storms and finally for the measurement of micro-meteorites. Within a few years the program and the tasks to be fulfilled by artificial satellites had expanded on an unforeseen scale.

On November 29, 1961 the Americans staged their dress rehearsal for a manned satellite flight after the Russians had already been successful in this respect. On that day the chimpanzee Enos orbited the earth twice in a Mercury capsule and returned safely. July 10, 1962 will remain memorable in the history of artificial satellites. On that day the first television satellite was successfully placed in orbit; it is described as an active relay satellite. The waves used for television transmissions travel in a straight line; over long distances transmission is, therefore, possible only with the aid of relay stations within visual distance of each other to pass on the program again and again. A television satellite is precisely such a relay station in space, which because of its great height, lies within the direct line of sight of a large area of the earth's surface. In the case of the first Telstar this area covered the entire width of the Atlantic Ocean, thereby making possible direct transmission of television programs from Europe to America and vice versa. The funeral ceremonies of the assassinated President John F. Kennedy were relayed to Europe by such a satellite.

The first satellite of this type was given the name of Telstar I and it circles the earth at distances between 590 and 3,500 miles. Its orbital period is 158 minutes. It made possible not only direct television transmissions but also transatlantic telephone conversations through space. A fault developed at the end of November, 1962, but scientists of the Bell Telephone Laboratories succeeded, by means of suitable radio signals from earth, in reactivating Telstar at the beginning of January, 1963. However, it failed again on February 21. This was the earth's first commercial television satellite. Telstar I gave excellent service and provided intercontinental television and telephone communications between Andover (U.S.A.) and Goonhilly (England) as well as Andover and Pleumeur-Bodou (France.) The first public television transmission from U.S.A. to Europe and vice versa took place on July 23, 1962.

Telstar I was followed on May 7, 1963 by the launching of Telstar II. Owing to the comparatively short orbital period of the two Telstars (Telstar I circles the earth once in 157·6 minutes) the amount of time available for transmission, for example between America and Europe, is very limited. Good reception is possible only for approximately fifteen minutes. For that reason a further type of communication satellite was created, which was given the name of Syncom. These Syncom satellites are placed in what are referred to as stationary orbits. We know that the farther away from earth a satellite orbits, the longer it will take to complete one orbit. The satellites nearest to earth have a period of approximately one and a half hours, the balloon satellite Echo I at an altitude of 1,000 miles completed one orbit every two hours. We can now imagine that at a certain distance from earth the orbital period will be twenty-four. This is the case at an altitude of 22,300 miles. That means that the satellite appears to stand still above one point of the earth's surface. In the case of communication satellites this has the great advantage that a permanent link can be provided between two continents, for example between America and Africa. An attempt to put Syncom I into a stationary orbit on February 14, 1963 was unsuccessful but Syncom II attained the calculated orbit on July 26, 1963 and has been working ever since.

Syncom II carries 3,840 silicon cells, fitted on the side faces; they generate electric current by converting sunlight into electricity. Owing to its great altitude, Syncom II is almost continuously exposed to sunlight so that the batteries can be recharged almost all the time. In addition to telecommunication equipment, Syncom also carries a large number of scientific instruments for recording internal and

60

external temperatures, current supply and observational data from space.

Syncom is a pioneer because with only three Syncom satellites it will be possible, probably in the near future, to span the globe and to connect all parts of the world with each other. Three telecommunication satellites spaced at equal distances in a stationary orbit will, for example, enable a single television program to be broadcast to the whole world, with the exception of the polar regions which are in any event uninhabitable.

By their scientific results, unmanned artificial satellites have paved the way for man into space but they have also achieved practical significance. Weather and communication satellites have already paid for themselves and will in future become even more important.

In addition to their scientific and practical importance, artificial satellites of Type Syncom have another, perhaps the most important, part to play. They will make possible world television. *One* program can be relayed to the whole world, and all mankind will, in a manner of speaking, sit in front of a single television screen. For example, a sporting event which is of universal interest can at the same instant also be witnessed by people on the other side of the globe. All mankind has thus become one large family; people are moved closer to each other and youth, which is particularly ready for new ideas, will have an opportunity of getting to know young people from other countries and other nations—in short, television satellites are important links between nations.

Cape Kennedy—Stepping Stone into Space

Vast installations, exceeding by far the equipment of an airport, are required for launching an artificial satellite or a manned space vehicle. The Spanish navigator Ponce de Leon, who discovered the Florida Peninsula in 1512, could not have dreamed that one day people would fly into space from this uninviting piece of land covered with dunes, marshes, lagoons, mangroves and low bushes. However, a sparsely populated, inhospitable stretch of coast is exactly the right place for launching rockets four and a half centuries later.

From Cape Kennedy the range is wide open, in front of it extends the vastness of the Atlantic Ocean, the area around the beach is very flat, thereby facilitating the construction of roads and launching pads. In addition, the subtropical climate (Cape Kennedy lies at a latitude of 28° N) is highly suitable and permits uninterrupted operation all the year round. Its full official name is "Air Force Missile Test Center" because originally the installations were used exclusively for testing American Air Force rockets. The whole area, which extends over many miles, and may be entered only with a special permit, is subdivided into "Complexes." These are the launching bases for the different types of rockets, Redstone, Jupiter, Titan, Atlas, Saturn, etc. Apart from the launching pads for the different rockets, the visitor will notice the associated blastproof concrete shelters for the launch command posts, as well as radio and telemetering equipment, radar instruments, assembly plant for the assembly rockets, fuel stores, factories for the production of lox (liquid oxygen) and the most advanced theodolites and cameras for tracking the space vehicles.

Let us take a closer look at the Jupiter Complex. It consists of four concrete launching pads, each measuring 200 by 200 feet. Each of these pads carries a structure, the launching platform where the rocket rests prior to launch. Thick strands of cables lead from each pad underground to the concrete blockhouse. We must not imagine this as a

The launch control center for Saturn rockets at Cape Kennedy contains all remote control equipment for launch and flight control.

romantic hut; we should rather think of a concrete pillbox located at a distance of approximately 100 yards from the launching pad and serving as control and command post. Here, the instrument readings showing the functioning of the individual parts of the rocket are evaluated and the final checks prior to launching are carried out by remote control.

The roof of a blockhouse consists of a ten-foot layer of concrete and above it a layer of two feet of sand. The entire blockhouse rests on resilient foundations so that it can "give" under the air pressure generated by the launch. The men inside the blockhouse are protected against all eventualities and are able to follow the launch through periscopes and on television screens.

On the launching platforms there are enormous lifting devices and

This picture was taken with a telelens. It shows the launch of an Atlas rocket and the service towers where the rockets are checked once again before launching.

service towers ready to raise the rockets into the launch position and serving as working platforms for the technicians. The service towers (from the distance they look similar to oil rigs) give Cape Kennedy a distinctive skyline, like the skyscrapers of New York. Within these towers, which are small, mobile skyscrapers, there are passenger and goods elevators taking people and materials up to the 28th floor.

Immediately prior to launch, the service tower rolls back on rails, thus

Giant assembly tower for a three-stage Saturn rocket.

releasing the rocket. Then begin the exciting last minutes of the countdown. The countdown is a carefully worked out minute-by-minute

The Kennedy Space Center at Cape Kennedy, Florida, during the Apollo countdown.

procedure for checking the function of the individual components of the space vehicle. During the final minutes before launching so many tests and commands are crowded together both inside the spaceship (if it is manned) and in the ground station, that the countdown ends with the counting of seconds.

At present the most gigantic structures at Cape Kennedy are the launching devices for the Saturn booster rockets. Their service towers, weighing 2,800 tons, are 312-foot tall travelling gantries made clearly visible from far away by their red-and-white paint. They contain their own compressed-air and electric-power lines, the most modern fire-fighting equipment and floodlights for work at night.

After a successful launch, when the rocket, carried by the reaction of the fiery jet from the nozzles, has risen from the white cloud of steam, the general control center takes over further observation. From there, the man in charge of the launching site checks the trajectory of the booster rocket and ascertains the course of its travel. If the rocket deviates from the predetermined course, all he has to do is press a button to destroy the rocket in the air.

All work on the testing grounds is carried out under the most stringent safety precautions. Not only do all the engineers shelter inside the blockhouse during the actual launch but even during preliminary work all possible precautions are taken. The entire staff working with rocket fuels wear a special type of protective clothing; the numerous firemen are equipped with asbestos suits and each launching complex can be completely flooded with water through a special piping system in a very short time.

Man in Space

The first man to shake off the bonds of the earth's gravity for any length of time and able to see the earth from the vantage point of space, was Yuri Gagarin who summarized his impressions as follows:

The ship had reached its trajectory, the wide road through space.

For all of us who live on earth, weightlessness is a very strange phenomenon. However, the organism quickly adapts to this condition. I felt a most unusual lightness in all limbs. I detached myself from the chair and floated between ceiling and floor of the cabin. The transition to this state of weightlessness takes place very gradually. As soon as the effect of gravity disappeared, I felt exceptionally well, everything had suddenly become much lighter. I felt as if my arms and legs and even my whole body no longer belonged to me, they no longer had any weight at all. I was neither sitting nor lying down, I appeared to be suspended somehow in the cabin. All objects that were not secured, floated about, and, looking at them, I thought I was dreaming. Map case, pencil and notebook floated through the cabin. A few droplets of liquid from a hose had assumed the shape of globules and drifted freely through the space. When they touched the walls of the cabin, they adhered to them like dew on a blossom.

At long last, I was on the journey of my life, on a flight around the world. At an altitude of 200 miles I thought gratefully about my great fortune in being the first man to fly through Cosmos and to be the first man able to report about it.

I saw the clouds and their shadows on the distant, beloved earth. For a moment the farmer's son awoke in me. The pitch-black sky looked like a freshly cultivated field and the stars were the seed grains. They shone bright and clear. The sun, too, was exceptionally bright; I was unable to observe it with unprotected eyes even when half closing them. The sun seemed many dozen times, perhaps even a hundred times brighter than on earth. It shone brighter than the liquid metal flowing from the furnace which I remember from my work in the foundry. At times I pushed the protective curtain in front of the porthole in order to reduce the glare from the sun.

I should have liked to see the moon as well. What might she look like in space? But unfortunately she remained outside my view during the flight. It doesn't matter, I thought; next time.

I observed not only the sky but also the earth. What did the oceans look like? They appeared as fairly dark, faintly shimmering spots. Was it possible to recognize the spherical shape of our planet? Yes, definitely. When I looked at the horizon I noticed a distinct contrasting transition from the bright surface of the earth to the completely black sky. The earth with its many tints was a pleasant sight. It was surrounded by a delicate blue aureole. The strip became darker and darker, turquoise, blue, violet and finally changed into pitch-black. This transition was a very beautiful sight.

When flying over the western hemisphere my thoughts turned to Columbus. He had discovered the New World with great effort and hardship. Its name, however, derived from Amerigo Vespucci who had thus, by means of the thirty-two pages of his book *Description of the New Countries* achieved immortality. I had read about this in a book by Stefan Zweig.

I looked around myself with excitement because I wanted to see everything, recognize and understand everything. Through the observation slits I was able to see the stars shimmering bright and cold like diamonds. The distance to the stars was still very great, perhaps ten light years or more, and yet, from my orbit they appeared much nearer than from earth. I was happy and at the same time slightly overawed by the thought that this spaceship had been entrusted to me—this precious treasure belonging to the State into which so much effort and money had been put.

So wrote the first Cosmonaut; a long road led to this achievement. Many years of technical, scientific and organizational preparations, many years of physical and mental training of the space travellers was necessary before a manned space flight could be attempted. And yet, in many ways it was a step into the unknown. The state of weightlessness

Yuri Gagarin, the first man in space.

prevailing during orbital flight could not be simulated on earth by any experimental arrangements. Only in parobolic flights, when the aircraft describes an arc open toward the earth, was it possible to achieve weightlessness for a maximum of one minute's duration. Would man's mental and physical reactions be normal under conditions of prolonged weightlessness? It was possible only to hope for this but not to forecast it with any certainty. We now know that the practical experience of manned space flight has led to an important discovery. Although man is born on earth, he is not tied to earth! Man is able to withstand the conditions of space flight and he is capable of undertaking even longer space flights.

The most important engineering problem to be solved was the design of a space vehicle, a spaceship which for Man represents a small piece of terrestrial environment accompanying him into space and enabling him to survive. The first task was to provide space travellers (the Russians call them Cosmonauts, the Americans Astronauts) with the necessary air, and to purify and enrich it with fresh oxygen to dispose of the used air. Next, care must be taken to provide a tolerable temperature; the interior of the spaceship must become neither too cold nor too hot. In the American Mercury capsules—the name given to the manned space vehicles launched by the U.S.A.—these tasks were accomplished by the life-support system in a most satisfactory manner. In the case of longer space journeys, the problem of nourishment and the disposal of body waste has to be solved. Under conditions of weightlessness, liquids cannot be taken to the mouth from a plate nor from a glass. During space flight it is impossible to eat soup with a spoon. Liquids must be introduced into the mouth from a squeeze tube. Solid food, such as sandwiches, biscuits, etc., do not present any difficulties even under conditions of weightlessness.

In the manned space flights carried out so far, eating, drinking, mental and physical work as well as sleep have taken place normally; the conditions of weightlessness did not present Man with any insurmountable obstacles during space flight.

Of course, hard training is still necessary before one is fit for space and all Astronauts have stories to tell about this. They are spun round in a centrifuge in order to learn how to withstand the high pressures occurring during launch and re-entry, which may rise to eight times the normal body weight. In the hot chamber, perspiration runs in streams underneath the space suit but the future space-man must not be put off by this. As a preparation for prolonged space journeys, future Astronauts allow themselves to be locked in an isolation chamber, a completely dark and soundproof compartment. Not everybody is therefore fit to become a space traveller. Only people with high mental and physical abilities and possessing an even temperament are suitable for space travel up to a certain age. The American John Glenn, aged 41, was the oldest Astronaut so far. He survived his flight extremely well.

71

All the Russian Cosmonauts were younger: their ages ranged between twenty and thirty years and they, too, have survived their space flights, most of them prolonged, without suffering any ill-effects.

In the case of manned satellite flights, the space capsule is placed into orbit by a booster rocket. The Americans used Atlas and Titan rockets for this purpose. Once in orbit, the capsule separates from the rocket and continues to circle the earth at the orbital speed without any propulsion. At that stage, the capsule has no longer any means of control, with the exception of the attitude control which can be operated either automatically or manually. However, the sole task of this control is to change the attitude of the capsule in space and it is unable to influence the orbit of the capsule in any way. This attitude control is of the utmost importance because during the return to earth the longitudinal axis of the bell-shaped capsule must assume a specified, slight inclination toward the horizon. The capsule races around the earth with its broad end forward. As long as the capsule is in orbit, the whole operation is virtually free of any danger. It only becomes exciting when re-entry begins. Fitted at the forward end are three retro-rockets with their nozzles pointing approximately in the direction of flight. When these retro-rockets (they operate with a solid propellant) are ignited, their reaction reduces the orbital speed, the balance between earth's gravity and centrifugal force is disturbed, the trajectory of the capsule is inclined toward earth as gravity has gained the upper hand, and, at an altitude of approximately sixty miles, the air friction becomes noticeable. The retro-rockets are jettisoned and the events which follow are a battle for the destruction of kinetic energy present in the space vehicle. At night, if a railway train brakes suddenly, we can see sparks flying from the wheels where the brakes press against the wheels. By comparison with the speed of a spaceship, the speed of a train is very low indeed. A natural phenomenon tells us what happens when a body enters the earth's atmosphere from space: the shooting stars and meteors light up and are usually burned up completely; only larger pieces survive the descent and later rest from their long cosmic trips in the form of stone or iron meteorites in various museums. The spaceship undergoes a similar experience and it is also heated to temperatures where it starts glowing, but it is absolutely vital that none of the heat developed on the outside can penetrate to the interior of the spaceship.

72

Top: The first experiments concerning weightlessness were carried out in diving aircraft. This picture shows Major General Oliver K. Niess (left) and Colonel John Paul Stapp (right,) floating under conditions of weightlessness. Colonel Stapp is trying to "drop" a coin. He is unable to do so because the coin also floats.

Bottom: To be able to withstand the enormous "g" forces during a rocket launch, the space pilots must gradually get used to increasing pressures of this kind. They can do so with the aid of a centrifuge, a roundabout fitted with exactly the same equipment as the space capsule. This centrifuge is spun at such a speed that the pilot is pressed against the seat with six times the pressure of his body weight. He must be able to withstand such a pressure at least for a short time because it corresponds to that experienced during an actual launch.

This heat problem has also been overcome.

The outside of the Mercury capsule consists of a high-temperature-resistant alloy which in addition is fitted in the form of roofing tiles, or scales, to increase the surface, which in turn facilitates the dissipation of heat. The main brunt is borne by the heat shield which is covered with a plastic lining. This melts away on entering the earth's atmosphere and evaporates. Evaporation consumes heat, and in this way it is possible to maintain the internal temperature of the capsule within limits bearable for the human occupant although temperatures of up to 2,550° F occur at the heat shield.

John Glenn gave a very vivid account of his return to earth:

> This business with the heat shield made re-entry into the earth's atmosphere rather dramatic. When I had reached the area of higher frictional heat, the glow started. It burned in bright orange flames outside the window. It became obvious that in the direction toward the heat shield something had broken away near the end of the capsule and large pieces of all sizes from a finger-tip to a diameter of up to approximately eight inches flew past the window from that direction. Well, it was the set of retro-rockets that was breaking up. But at the time I thought they had already been jettisoned. So there were a few moments of doubt whether the heat shield had been damaged or whether it was breaking up. That could have been a bad day. But it was a most impressive sight to watch this orange glow and the burning parts which kept flying past.

During this dramatic re-entry operation, Glenn never lost his sense of humour; but he said it was the most wonderful moment when he saw the first parachute deploying at an altitude of approximately eight miles. The final deceleration prior to landing on the earth's surface is provided by the parachutes. At first a drogue parachute is released. This small parachute has the job of stabilizing the descending capsule which is liable to start spinning in flight. Then the main parachute is opened which lowers the manned capsule to the earth's surface.

A parachute is at the mercy of wind and weather and since the capsule has no means of controlling its course, it is not possible to predict the point of landing accurately. The Americans arranged for their

Right: John H. Glenn walking to the launching pad of the Mercury Atlas rocket.

ar right: Cape Kennedy February 20, 1962, 0947 hours *local time:* the Atlas booster rocket of the Mercury *space* capsule "Friendship 7" during lift-off from the *launch* platform. Lt. Col. John H. Glenn at the be-*ginning* of his flight around the earth.

Mercury and Gemini capsules to splash down in the sea, most of them in the Atlantic Ocean, southeast of the Bahamas. There the recovery fleet was ready to pick up the capsule from the sea. While the Astronaut is still descending in his capsule by parachute, radio contact is re-established, the nearest ship hurries to the point of splashdown at full speed. The Astronaut is then released from his capsule unless he has climbed out before and has entered the inflatable dinghy. To facilitate the location of the Astronauts in the sea, the capsule floating on the water broadcasts radio signals, a green dye is released in the water and finally a smoke signal can be given as well. The Russian Cosmonauts came down on dry land with their space capsule descending by para-chute. Arrangements were made for the Cosmonaut to leave the capsule by ejector seat and to land by parachute on his own.

An enormous number of people are needed to insure the safety of one man during his flight around the earth. Even though the eyes of the whole world are trained on the space traveller, the Astronaut, we must not forget that his achievement is only the culmination of vast team-work. Many years of planning, scientific investigations, the work of skilled hands, careful tests, etc., have preceded the decisive moment. Whereas only a few years ago individual achievements were possible (let us remember, for example, Charles Lindbergh's first solo flight across the Atlantic,) today an individual can accomplish nothing without the pre-parations made and help given by other people. The co-operation of entire groups is a characteristic feature of our modern world at work. The first American satellite flight made by John Glenn involved the participation of 19,300 people. Of these, 300 men belonged to the launching personnel on Cape Kennedy and 15,600 men to the recovery force. For their project Mercury the Americans established eighteen tracking stations stretching like a chain around the whole world. This chain encompasses three continents as well as three oceans and uses tele-phone land lines, submarine cables as well as radio and other means of communication. The network comprises 100,000 miles of teleprinter lines, 34,000 miles of telephone lines and more than 5,000 miles of high-speed data transmission circuits. The equipment of the individual tracking station includes long-range radar for locating the space vehicle, as well as automatic tracking equipment, telemetering equipment for the reception of data from the Astronaut and the space capsule, command

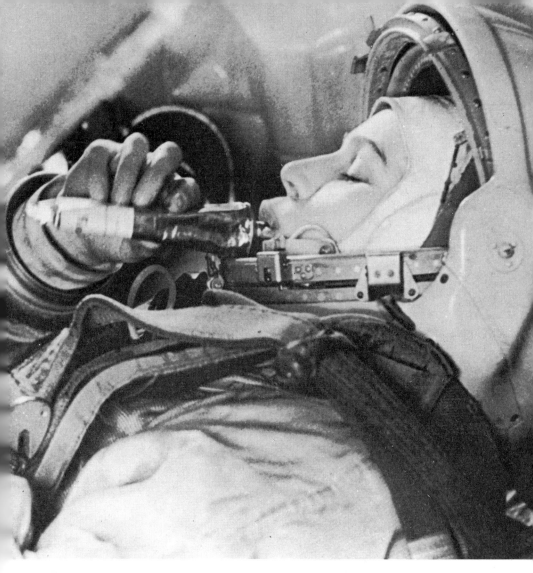

The first woman Cosmonaut, Valentina Tereshkova, taking a sip from the squeeze tube.

equipment for guiding the space vehicles from the ground, should this be necessary, and two-way radio-telephone links between space capsule and the ground. The tracking stations are also equipped with electronic computers which immediately process the telemetering information. These tracking and telemetering data are processed so quickly that the observer sitting in the middle can follow the events at the very instant they occur. This is called real or actual time.

Gemini 12, the capsule of the last manned Gemini flight with Astronauts James A. Lovell Jr., Chief Pilot (right,) and Edwin E. Aldrin, Jr.

The calculation results are speedily passed on to the Goddard Space Flight Center in Greenbelt, Maryland. There, the data concerning trajectory, flight control, temperature and other reports are immediately analyzed with the aid of a large electronic computer and compared with the advance calculations. The results are passed on to Cape Kennedy via high-speed circuits and there in the flight control center the decision is taken about the continuation of the space flight. From there all information is passed on to the tracking stations which are spread over the whole world. In this way these stations are instantly informed about the general situation at any given moment.

The telemetry data provide information not only about the trajectory, air pressure and temperature in the space capsule but also about the Astronauts' physical condition at all times. During flight, the Astronauts have medical probes fixed directly to their bodies to provide information about body temperature, heartbeat and breathing. These data are transmitted to the ground stations where experts in space medicine supervise the flight from a medical point of view.

Man in space is thus in constant contact with earth; he can talk to his colleagues and he is constantly under observation. The situation of explorers has changed radically within a few decades. We can regard space travellers as explorers penetrating into undiscovered, new territories. For example, only sixty years ago, a polar expedition lost all contact with the outside world on leaving their last port of call. Many years passed before certainty was established about the expedition's fate. A tragic example is the attempt of the Swedish engineer S. A. Andrée to fly over the North Pole in a balloon. He left Spitzbergen with two companions on July 8, 1897. The balloon, called "Eagle," flew off at great speed in a northerly direction. There were no radio transmitters in those days. With luck, carrier pigeons and messages in bottles were able to provide news. Andrée disappeared and no trace of his balloon was found until the summer of 1930, when thirty-three years after their departure, their bodies were found, together with diaries, books and exposed photographic plates which were developed with especial care after such a long time.

Sixty years after Andrée's ill-fated expedition the first artificial satellite was launched and the radio link with space vehicles was never broken off, on the contrary it was developed in a manner undreamed of.

We must remember that manned space flight was made possible not only by progress in the field of rocketry but also by the development of other branches of engineering, above all telecommunications and electronic computers.

Manned satellite flights are only preliminary exercises to prepare for manned space flights to more distant targets and for the construction of orbiting space stations. The technical means available at present require the development of methods for bringing together two or more space vehicles in one orbit, for example, for the purpose of refuelling a spaceship. The Russians have already carried out two group flights for studying this rendezvous technique: the first as early as 1962 and the second in 1963. On August 11, Andrian Nikolayev went into orbit in Vostok III and was joined almost exactly twenty-four hours later by Pavel Popovich in Vostok IV. The purpose of this exercise was to gather experience about the co-ordinated actions of two Cosmonauts and the effect of identical space-flight conditions on their organisms. But above all it was to attempt a linkup of orbiting spaceships. The accuracy required in the launching of the second spaceship presented great difficulties. For example, if the launching is delayed by only five seconds, this will cause a difference in the trajectory of eighteen to twenty-five miles, making a rendezvous doubtful. It must therefore be regarded as a great achievement that the Russians were able to bring the two space vehicles Vostok III and Vostok IV to within three and a half miles of each other.

During the second Russian group flight of Vostok V and Vostok VI, the two space vehicles also approached each other and this time to a distance of three miles. The spaceship Vostok V with Cosmonaut Valeri Bykovski on board was launched at 1500 hours Moscow time on June 14, 1963. The perigee of the orbit was 112 miles and apogee 143 miles. The initial orbital period was 88·4 minutes. On June 16, 1963 at 1230 hours the first woman went into space. The name of the first woman Cosmonaut is Valentina Vladimirovna Tereshkova. The launch was successful and proceeded according to plan. Valentina Tereshkova's earth orbit differed only slightly from that of Bykovski. Vostok VI took 88·3 minutes to complete one orbit and its perigee and apogee were 113 and 145 miles respectively. The two spaceships were in radio telephone communication with each other and during flight, television transmissions from space were relayed to earth. Valeri Bykovski gave an example of the grotesque state of weightlessness and presented himself to the astonished viewers floating upside-down in his cabin. He returned to his contoured seat and then carried out a further very strange experiment. Under the conditions of weightlessness water does not behave in the way we are used to. For example, a vessel is unnecessary since, if handled carefully, water will form into a sphere as a result of surface tension. Bykovski allowed a large sphere of water to float through the cabin, blew on it without breaking it up and then he took this sphere carefully between his hands and released it again. It all looked like magic. Valentina Tereshkova also performed a few "tricks" for the benefit of her television audience. She let a pencil and her logbook float about in the cabin.

At that time Russian space exploits were going from strength to strength. The double flights of the Vostok spaceships carrying one Cosmonaut each, were followed on October 12, 1964 by the first launch of a spaceship with more than one man on board, thus heralding a new development in manned space flights. For the first time, three Cosmonauts travelled in a single space capsule (it was called "Voskhod," meaning "sunrise") orbiting the earth and for the first time they travelled without wearing spacesuits, showing their supreme confidence in the technical perfection of the space vehicle. The commander of Voskhod was Vladimir Komarov, the scientist was Constantin Feoktistov and the doctor on board was Boris Yegorov. They circled the earth sixteen times in twenty-four hours and seventeen minutes and reached a maximum distance of 250 miles. The highly successful Cosmonaut Komarov lost his life in tragic circumstances when Soyus I crashed on April 24, 1967.

Once more Soviet spacemen had scored a "first." On March 18, 1965, Voskhod 2 was sent into orbit with Colonel Pavel Belyayev (Commander) and Lt.-Colonel Alexei Leonov (co-pilot.) For the first time a human being dared to leave the shelter of the space capsule and step into empty space. This first space walk took twenty minutes and the flight of Voskhod 2 was successfully concluded after twenty-six hours.

Leaving the space capsule while in orbit is only a necessary step in the further development of space travel because future tasks will require outside work. Especially during the assembly of space vehicles in space, such outside work will have to be carried out under conditions of

A Mercury capsule floating in the sea being recovered by helicopter.

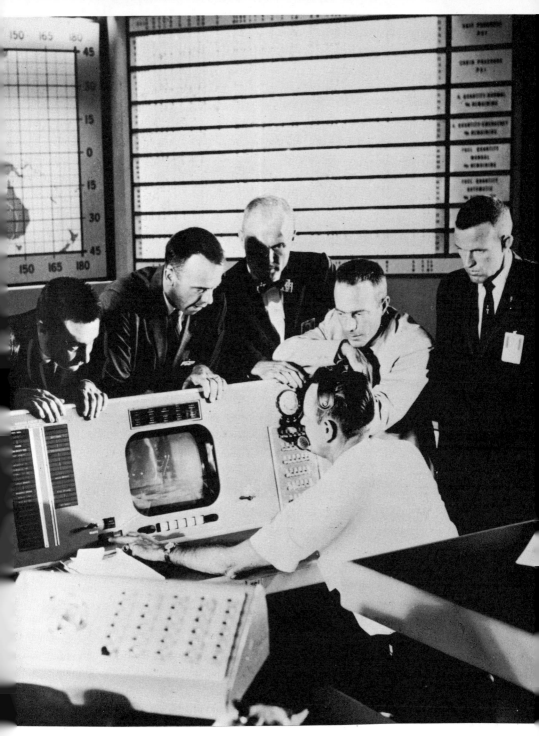

A specialist explaining to the American Astronauts the action of a control screen. Standing from left to right the seven Astronauts: Clayton, Schirra, Grissom, Shepard, Glenn, Carpenter and Cooper.

weightlessness. With their Gemini project the Americans have done outstanding pioneering work aimed at meeting these requirements of space travel.

All space travel is directed toward one main aim: to land a man on the moon. Among the most important preparations for this are rendezvous and docking techniques.

They were the main features of the Gemini program which was concluded with the flight of Gemini 12. The object was to "catch" an unmanned Agena target satellite (length approximately thirty-three feet, diameter five feet.) After the target satellite had entered orbit, the Gemini capsule was injected into the same orbit in such a manner that it would enter its own orbit as near as possible to the target satellite.

The Gemini capsule had room for two Astronauts (Gemini is Latin for "twins".) Its length was eighteen feet and its width at the base ten feet. In shape the Gemini capsule is very similar to the Mercury capsule but is about three times as heavy. The Gemini capsule was lifted by a Titan II booster rocket. This type is fitted with two stages, with the first one developing a thrust of 194 tons. The entire combination of Titan II together with the Gemini capsule was 108 feet tall. The fuel used by Titan II is monomethylhydracin and unsymmetrical dimethylhydracin mixed at a ratio of 50 : 50 and the oxidant is nitrogentetroxide. The fuel mixture and oxidant form a hypergol, a self-igniting mixture, making a separate ignition system unnecessary.

After entering orbit the Gemini Astronauts had to steer their spaceship toward the target satellite. In addition to a radio transmitter the target satellite also carries two acquisition lights flashing eighty times per minute and visible from a distance of twenty-three miles.

The approach to the target satellite presented the Astronauts with a new problem because steering in empty space is completely different from the steering technique of jet or propeller-driven aircraft. Aircraft still move in a resisting medium—the earth's atmosphere. By moving the elevators and rudder, any desired change in direction can be initiated. In the virtually empty space, any change of direction can be achieved only by the reaction of a supporting mass. In orbit this leads to phenomena which seem surprising at first sight. Let us assume that a spaceship is travelling around the earth in a circular orbit and that its speed is then reduced with the aid of its retro-rockets acting exactly opposite to the direction of motion, that is to say tangentially to the circular orbit. The result is a change of orbit: the circular orbit is changed into an ellipse with its perigee within the original circular orbit. However, according to Kepler's law, the spaceship will travel faster as it comes near to earth, so that the effect of braking will in fact be an increase in speed! However, starting from the perigee of the new elliptical orbit, the spaceship will again be decelerated until it has reached the point farthest away from earth and then the cycle begins afresh. We can thus see that in questions of steering in space the real experts are the astronomers because the problem is basically one of astronomical orbit calculations.

By suitably braking and accelerating with the aid of small rocket engines, the Gemini Astronauts were able to learn within an astonishingly short time the art of steering in space. However, the Gemini spaceships were not yet equipped for drastic changes of orbit. They could be regarded as fully maneuverable spaceships only after docking to the Agena target satellite. The approach to the Agena took place at a slow walking speed of one mile per hour until the nose cone of the Gemini capsule was pushed into the funnel-shaped aperture of the Agena, the docking adaptor. A guideway in the funnel insured that docking took place in such a manner that all the electrical contacts between Gemini and the Agena target rocket were made correctly so that the Agena target rocket could be ignited from the Gemini capsule. Since the target satellite reached space without any loss of fuel (it was placed into orbit by an Atlas booster rocket) the Gemini capsule became highly maneuverable after docking and was able to carry out substantial changes in orbital height and orbital inclination.

The Americans have completed ten Gemini flights without incident, even though not always according to schedule.

Shortly after Leonov's space walk, NASA (National Aeronautics and Space Administration) in America started its first manned Gemini flight with Gemini 3. This flight was of short duration and its purpose was merely to test the capsule with Astronauts Virgil I. Grissom and John W. Young orbiting the earth three times on March 23, 1965 in four hours fifty-three minutes. The flights of Gemini 1 and Gemini 2 were unmanned test flights. Gemini 1 orbited the earth four times and then burned out in the earth's atmosphere, Gemini 2 merely carried out

85

Part of the moon panorama transmitted by Luna 13. Lunar landscape in the Ocean of Storms.

a ballistic flight in order to test the fitness of the capsule on re-entry into the earth's atmosphere. The flight of Gemini 4 from June 3 to June 7, 1967 was the beginning of a new era in manned space flights. The pilot, Edward H. White, left the capsule, like his Soviet colleague, Leonov, to make a space walk, but he used for the first time a hand-held propulsion gun. In American space terminology a space walk is referred to as "extra-vehicular activity."

Exit into space requires a particularly safe spacesuit and an absolutely fault-free supply of the necessary breathing air. The actual exit does not present any difficulties. When the Astronaut steps out into Nothing after opening the hatch, no wind will tear him back, although he is circling the earth at a speed of 17,400 miles per hour, neither will he drop back to earth from a height of, say, 125 miles because the centrifugal force protects him against crashing. He simply floats away from the capsule at the speed with which he pushed himself away. The space traveller would continue to fly away farther and farther without stopping and—what a dreadful thought—would drift away from the space capsule unless he were held by a cable or if the hand-held propulsion gun allowed him to float back. There is no footpath in empty

View into the moon crater Copernicus from a height of 28 miles. Telephoto taken by Lunar Orbiter II on November 23, 1966. When this picture was taken, the centre of Copernicus was approximately 150 miles away from the camera. The hills inside the crater are approximately 1,000 ft. high; at the horizon can be seen the peaks of the moon Carpathians.

space against which the soles of the spacesuit could push to start walking back. The Astronaut can either haul himself back along a line or arrange for the reaction of the hand-held propulsion gun to take place in the desired direction to enable him to float back to the capsule. On their first space walk the Americans used compressed oxygen in their hand-held propulsion guns and the Astronaut was doubly secured by the "line" (the cable) because through this cable the "space walker" was also supplied with fresh air while the used air was drawn off by a different system of tubes within the cable.

The Americans use pure oxygen for breathing in all their manned space flights. Following the tragic fire on board the Apollo capsule which caused the death of the three Astronauts Grissom, White and Chaffee, fierce arguments started about the relative merits of the pure-oxygen method and the two-gas method. The Russians had decided on the use of the two-gas method, and their Cosmonauts in the spaceships breathed the same air as at home. Neither of the two methods is perfect; both have their advantages and their disadvantages, and both involve a certain amount of risk and also the danger of fire. Man has unfortunately not yet learned to design a "perfect machine." Our atmosphere is made up of approximately four-fifths nitrogen and one-fifth oxygen. Nitrogen serves virtually only to dilute the oxygen. If it is omitted, the rest is of course perfectly adequate for breathing. Omitting the nitrogen results in a substantial saving in weight, a most powerful argument where space travel is concerned, so that the Americans decided on an internal pressure in the cabin of roughly one-third normal pressure at sea level, using pure oxygen. An internal pressure corresponding to atmospheric pressure on earth would have meant making the cabin even tighter and providing additional insulating layers on the outside, which would have made the capsule much heavier.

The choice of a nitrogen-oxygen atmosphere forced the Russian designers to fit large steel containers on the outside of their spaceships, with valves opening inward. The pressure in the cabins corresponded roughly to atmospheric pressure on earth. This was the reason why the outside of the Vostok and Voskhod spaceships had to be heavily plated in order to avoid any significant losses of pressure.

A particularly serious disadvantage of the two-gas method became apparent during Leonov's space walk. The Cosmonaut leaving his spaceship must be able to move freely and carry out various tasks. However, a spacesuit with an internal pressure of fourteen pounds per square inch becomes so rigid that the wearer cannot move his arms and legs. Any reduction in the pressure would, however, mean that the amount of oxygen available is reduced to a dangerously low level.

In the Soviet space program this difficulty was overcome in the only Russian space walk carried out so far, by changing the mixing ratio of oxygen and nitrogen before leaving the spaceship. This, however, required a very complex procedure lasting several hours, similar to the pressure equalization which a deep-sea diver has to undergo in a decompression chamber after having spent a long time in very deep water.

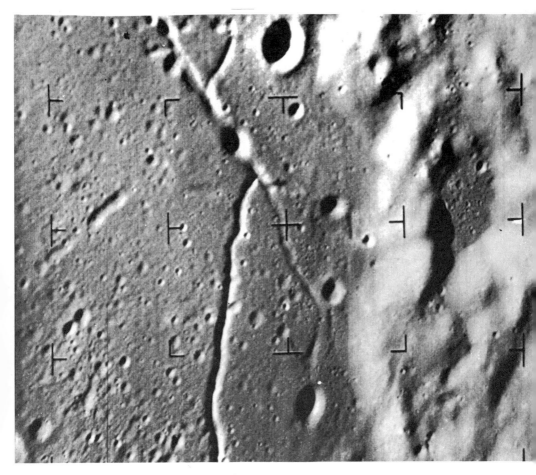

The eastern edge of the crater Alphonsus with rills and numerous small craters. This picture was relayed by Ranger IX one minute and 16 seconds before impact, from an altitude of 115 miles above the surface of the moon.

The Americans also considered a two-gas system, using oxygen and very light helium, such as is used by the Aquanauts (underwater explorers) for prolonged diving experiments, but this idea was soon rejected. Breathing of this gas mixture changes a normal human voice into a kind of high-pitched squeaking sound (like that we know so well from Walt Disney's Donald Duck films) and this could seriously endanger the safety of radio telephone communication between spaceship and ground stations. It may therefore be assumed that the Americans will retain the pure oxygen method and will only increase the safety measures.

A physical phenomenon occurring under conditions of weightlessness should be mentioned. If an open flame is not moved, it will be suffocated by its own waste gases almost at once because the gases cannot rise. On earth they rise immediately due to their increased temperature so that fresh air carrying oxygen is drawn in underneath. In a spaceship the head of a match, for example, would burn because the compound contains an oxygen carrier, but the wood would not burn any farther because it would be suffocated by its own combustion products. Only a moving match would burn as fresh air is constantly added to it. The disastrous fire in the Apollo capsule did not occur in space but on the test pad.

With Gemini 7 (Commander: Frank Borman, Pilot: James Lovell) the Gemini flights were extended to a period of almost fourteen days. Such a time would be sufficient for a flight to the moon and back, including one week's stay. Gemini 6, which was launched eleven days later than Gemini 7, approached Gemini 7, changing its original elliptical orbit (altitude 100 to 165 miles) into circular orbit at an altitude of 185 miles and five hours and forty-seven minutes after launch it approached the second spaceship and came within twelve inches of it. The crews were able to see each other through the portholes and exchange visual signals. This was the first space rendezvous of two spaceships travelling around the earth in one orbit. The Gemini Astronauts carried out twenty experiments, among them experiments relating to space medicine, the acuity of vision in space and the transmission of signals by laser rays.

The power supply of the Gemini spaceships was provided mainly by fuel cells in which hydrogen and oxygen are combined into water by a cold process while simultaneously electrical energy is liberated. The water obtained as a by-product was used for the space travellers.

During prolonged space flights it is, of course, essential to make sure that the Astronauts receive food. Eating under conditions of weightlessness does not present any particular difficulties. Swallowing and further movements of food take place normally. When compiling a menu for the Astronauts, attention had to be paid to a concentrated and low-residue diet. During the flight of Gemini 11, planned to last three days, each

Astronaut was provided with ten meals, consisting of two types of nourishment: ready-to-eat food and food made edible only by the addition of water. The dehydrated foodstuffs were mixed with water by means of a special device. The "pantry" was fitted above the pilot's right-hand shoulder. All foodstuffs were wrapped in plastic covers and aluminum foil. There were three different menus which were eaten in strict order, the calories having been accurately calculated for each menu.

Menu A: Fruit salad, roasted oatmeal, bacon slices, ham, apple purée, cinnamon pastry, orange juice and pineapple-and-grapefruit juice. Of these items only the bacon slices and the cinnamon pastry were ready for eating, all the rest were dehydrated. Number of calories 707.

Menu B: Crab hors d'oeuvre, chicken, toast, pineapple pastry, orange-and-grapefruit juice, coconut cubes. Number of calories 883.

Menu C: Roast beef, potato salad, cinnamon pastry, chocolate pudding, honey pastry, tea. Number of calories 898.

Such a diet does not cause wind and is tasty and varied.

Body waste products are removed by special extraction devices fitted into the spacesuit since it is impossible to move about inside the cramped Gemini capsule. With Gemini 8, Gemini flights resulted in the first successful docking operation with the Agena Target Satellite but because of a short circuit the mission had to return to earth earlier than planned. During the flight of Gemini 9, Eugene Cernan's space walk lasted two hours and five minutes; he circled the earth as a "living moon" two and a half times: he experienced sunrise and sunset every forty-five minutes. The spacesuit proved highly successful both in the relentless heat of the sun on the day side of the earth as well as in the bitter cold on the night side.

With the aid of the rocket engines of the docked Agena rocket, it was possible to extend the flight of Gemini 10 to an altitude of 475 miles; however, this record was short-lived because Gemini 11 reached an altitude of 865 miles, thus penetrating into the radiation belt surrounding the earth, without any ill effects on the Astronauts, Charles Conrad Jr. and Richard F. Gordon. The flight of Gemini 11 resulted in the first direct ascent rendezvous, an exceptionally difficult operation made possible only by the computer and radar equipment on board. The amount of assistance required from ground control was only very small. Gordon's planned space walk of two and a half hours had to be given

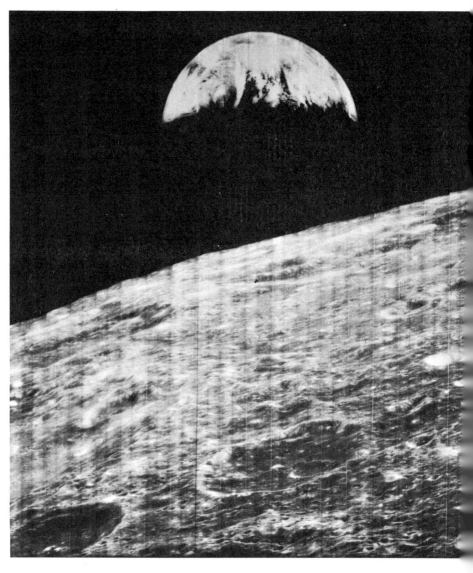

The first successful photograph of earth taken from near the moon by Lunar Orbiter II. The negative taken on Kodak High Resolution Aerial Film was developed in the space probe and radioed to earth as negative.

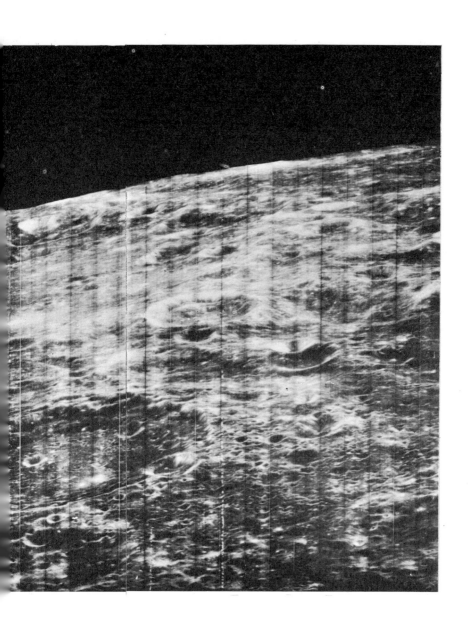

up after forty-four minutes because of excessive perspiration. His visor became fogged and the air conditioning plant of his spacesuit was overloaded. However, before abandoning the experiment, Gordon was able to connect the Gemini spaceship to the Agena rocket by a 330-foot length of Dacron rope. The Gemini capsule then "accelerated" and the two space vehicles began to rotate about each other. This is how artificial gravity was generated in space for the first time; it amounted to 0·00015 of normal terrestrial gravitation. Under such gravitation a body will fall three hundredths of one inch during the first second.

The last Gemini flight (Gemini 12) brought about a further important advance. Aldrin left his space vehicle for two hours nine minutes and for the first time a human being floating freely in space, worked outside, thereby proving the possibility of connecting parts, which have been placed into orbit. The Americans are planning to establish a manned laboratory orbiting the earth in the near future (MOL = Manned Orbital Laboratory.) The Gemini flights were an indispensable preparation for the realization of the MOL project and for future manned flights to the moon.

The flight of the Russian spaceship Soyus 1 with the Cosmonaut Komarov on board ended in disaster: the braking parachute failed, the spaceship crashed to the ground and broke up. (See table of manned space flights on page 127.)

Target Moon

Roughly at the same time as manned space travel was developed, the exploration of nearby planets with unmanned space vehicles began. Probes were sent not only to the moon but also to Venus inside, and Mars outside the earth's orbit around the sun. The first task, however, was the exploration of the moon's surface. This took place in stages, always with a view to the future manned flight to the moon. First of all the moon had to be hit. This was achieved as early as 1959. In that year the first photographs of the reverse side of the moon were taken; both of these successes were achieved by the Soviet Union. The main efforts of astronautics were, however, aimed at finding out whether the moon's surface was suitable for landing spacecraft. An answer to this question was obtainable only if it proved possible to transmit close-up pictures of the moon's surface to earth.

The greatest technological difficulties were presented by a soft landing on the moon. The problem was how to land a space vehicle so gently that the instruments on board would remain undamaged. As the moon has no blanket of air, landing by parachute is impossible. Only the reaction of a rocket engine can slow down the descent toward the moon's surface. Originally, the Americans had planned a soft landing on the moon, with their Ranger project but after several unsuccessful attempts (for example, Ranger IV, launched on April 23, 1962, crashed because the retro-rockets had failed) they boldly changed their program by dispensing with a soft landing and accepting the destruction of the probe. In return, they had hoped to obtain in rapid succession close-up pictures of the moon's surface. The Ranger moon probes were fitted with six television cameras; their total weight was in the region of 805 pounds. The six cameras had different focal lengths and a different number of lines per image. The long-focus cameras had a 25 millimeter lens with a relative aperture of f : 1 and a 75 millimeter lens of f : 1 with 1,150 lines per image, compared with 525 to 625 lines of most of the American

TV systems. The four p-cameras had a longer focal length and transmitted smaller pictures of 300 lines each but they transmitted one picture every 0·2 seconds and the f-cameras one picture every 2·56 seconds.

The flight to the moon took place in two stages. At first the booster carried the probe into a parking orbit around the earth from which it entered a transit orbit to the moon at a moment calculated by electronic computers. At that time the velocity was close to six miles per second and was permitted to deviate from the calculated value by not more than twenty-three feet per second. The two "sun sails" were extended by an automatic release device and the solar batteries were orientated toward the sun with the aid of a positioning rocket controlled by pulses from the sun sensors. Following this, the key-shaped main aerial was aligned directly toward the ground station by intricate maneuvers. A mid-course correction sixteen hours after launch, involving the ignition of a small rocket motor and orientation of the probe in space by radio signals, resulted in an accuracy bordering on the fabulous. With an average distance of the moon of 236,000 miles the deviation from the intended point of impact was only about ten miles.

Three probes of the Ranger type (Ranger VII, VIII and IX) together returned a total of more than 17,000 photographs of the moon's surface, starting from a distance of approximately 1,250 miles to shortly before impact from an altitude of three quarters of a mile. In the last pictures, details measuring only three feet across are visible. The pictures taken by Ranger IX, which crashed inside the large crater Alphonsus in the middle of that half of the moon facing us, are of particularly excellent quality and are extremely interesting since they indicate that an eruption of ash has taken place comparatively recently. A most important discovery made possible by the photographs taken by the Ranger spacecraft was the presence of small craters with a diameter of three feet and less which cover the moon's surface in tremendous numbers and in comparatively uniform distribution. There is no doubt that they are craters formed by the impact of meteors.

The Ranger spacecraft fulfilled their missions at the moment of impact. They were destroyed after hitting the moon at a speed of 8,530 feet per second. Successful as the Ranger missions were, they remained one-sided in one respect: the pictures returned by the Ranger space-

Recovery test of Apollo capsule. The picture shows the Astronauts Chief Pilot Virgil Grissom (leaving the floating capsule,) Edward White (left) and Roger Chaffee (already in the rubber dinghy) who were subsequently killed in an accident on the ground.

craft always showed the moon's surface from a "bird's eye view" and never from ground level. To see the moon landscape also from ground view, which is absolutely essential for the preparation of a manned landing, the problem of "soft" landing had to be solved.

Following the successes scored by Ranger spacecraft, the Russian space technologists also began to concentrate on this task. At first one failure was followed by another and this is not surprising because the soft landing represents an extremely delicate problem, requiring an accurate co-ordination of the retro-rockets and approach to the moon's surface. If the retro-rocket is switched off too soon, the spacecraft will crash from too great a height and the instruments will be destroyed. Although the gravity action of the moon's surface is only one-sixth of terrestrial gravity, a drop from a height of several yards can have serious results. Let us imagine what would happen if we dropped a television set from a height of three feet! Luna 8, launched on December 3, 1965, almost brought the desired success; it soft landed on the moon but unfortunately the transmitter failed so that the television camera was unable to relay any pictures. Only the fifth attempt was successful. Luna 9 landed on February 3, 1966 on the floor of *Oceanus Procellarum* (Ocean of Storms) without any damage and the television camera relayed to earth the first close-up pictures of the lunar surface as well as a moon panorama.

With present-day equipment a flight to the moon would take about $68\frac{1}{2}$ hours. The *Oceanus Procellarum* which to the naked eye appears at the bottom left-hand edge of the moon disc, was chosen as the landing area for good reasons. On the one hand it is an extensive plain which, as far as could be foreseen, would offer a suitable terrain. Secondly, it was possible to select the moment of landing in such a manner that the probe would reach the moon at sunrise, thus having fourteen terrestrial days of continuous lunar day, and assuring the television camera of fourteen days' light. For the first time, man had an opportunity to see a moon landscape as if he were himself standing on the moon's surface. It was not long before the first American probe, Surveyor, made a successful soft landing on the moon at the first attempt, coming down in the *Oceanus Procellarum*, and transmitting pictures of the moonscape from a ground level view. They are strangely fascinating. The sunflooded landscape is topped by a pitch-black sky and the actual scenery is different from what was previously assumed: there is no dust into which the landing legs of the probe could have sunk, but the area is strewn with stones and rocks of different sizes and all these pieces and all elevations show gently rounded outlines. Luna 13 and Surveyor III were soft landed in the Ocean of Storms and both tried to discover the load-carrying capacity of the moon's surface by practical experiments. Luna 13 was fitted with a dynamograph operating with a plunger for measuring the ground. A powder jet unit developing a pressure of approximately fifteen pounds presses a plunger against the lunar surface. A comparison of the data provided by the dynamograph and the model experiments on earth gave rise to the assumption that the mechanical properties of the upper lunar layer to a depth of about twelve to sixteen inches are roughly identical to medium-density ground on earth. An attempt to determine the specific gravity of the lunar substance produced surprisingly low values with a maximum of one gram per cubic centimeter (0.036 pounds/inch^3) indicating a very porous structure, as is also revealed by close-up pictures of the lunar surface showing a pronounced granular structure with a grain size of a few millimeters. Similar results were achieved by the American Surveyor III which was carried into a transfer orbit by an Atlas-Centaur booster rocket and was soft landed upright on the lunar surface with the aid of a small computer-controlled rocket motor. Surveyor III is fitted with a small dredger capable of digging trenches two inches wide and up to eighteen inches long and presenting the dug-up material to the lens of the television camera. The dredger is fitted to an arm which can be extended up to five feet. According to investigations carried out with the aid of this dredger, the lunar surface has the same load-carrying capacity as wet sea-shore sand. The dredger also picked up small stones and there is reason to believe that the floor of *Oceanus Procellarum* is able to support the Apollo mission's lunar excursion module weighing approximately eleven tons.

One thing must, however, be borne in mind as far as all these successes are concerned: tests have so far been made only at four points of the lunar surface and these are all located in the same area, the *Oceanus Procellarum*. It was necessary to adopt a different method for exploring other possible landing sites. Large parts of the lunar surface had to be inspected and searched for suitable landing sites. This has led to the launching of the orbiter probes designed to orbit the moon but not to land on it. They were aimed for a fly-by of the moon and their speed was suitably reduced at the right moment to enable them to be "captured" by the moon. They thus became moons of our moon, able to carry out important tasks while in orbit. The first orbiters were sent around the moon by the Russians. A beginning was made with Luna 10 but that probe had no optical instruments on board, neither had Luna 11. The American Lunar Orbiter I was the first to take photographs

Vehicle Assembly Building for the Apollo spaceship showing Complex 39A in the background, the starting point for space flights to the moon.

while circling the moon, using a special camera. It is fitted with two lenses. One has a focal length of 71 centimeters and a speed of f : 5·6. With this lens it is possible to obtain pictures on which objects measuring three feet across are discernible. The other lens has a focal length of 7·5 centimeters and a speed of f: 4·5. With the aid of this lens, objects measuring twenty-five feet across can be recognized if the moon is photographed from a height of approximately twenty-eight miles. The camera was loaded with a special low-sensitivity black-and-white film of high resolution. With each exposure, two pictures were taken simultaneously, covering an area of twenty-four by nineteen miles and ten by two and a half miles respectively. During development the film was brought into contact with a Bimat film, a special film treated with chemicals. These develop and fix the film in 3·4 minutes. The Bimat film is then rolled up, while the photographic film is hot-dried in 11·5 minutes before being passed to the transmission system. There, the picture is scanned by a powerful pin-point source of light and converted into electrical pulses which are transmitted to earth by radio. The 70-millimeter film is broken up into 18,942 lines for the purpose of transmission and, as a result, the pictures contain approximately 2,400 times more detail than could be displayed on an ordinary television screen. The system requires approximately forty-five minutes for transmitting one picture and transmission can take place only when the spaceship flies facing earth and when the solar cells supply the power required for transmission. The Orbiters provided the first large-area photographs of the moon, distinguished by remarkable clarity. They also show the first picture of earth, floating freely above the lunar horizon as a heavenly object showing approximately half-phase. Lunar Orbiters IV and V circling the moon from comparatively far away are designed to provide information for a general photographic chart of the moon.

On September 15, 1968, the Soviet Union launched an automatic space station, Sonde 5. For the first time an unmanned spacecraft has circled the moon and returned to earth. Sonde 5 came down in the Indian Ocean at 19.08 hours Moscow time on September 21 and was recovered by a Soviet search vessel on the 22nd. During the flight, the space station's systems and equipment for maneuvering in flight and for the return to earth were tried and conditions in space in the vicinity of the moon were also explored.

The gigantic crawler in front of the Assembly Building designed for transporting the Saturn V booster rocket with the Apollo capsule on top (height approximately 367 feet, weight 2,819 tons) to the launching pad on Merritts Island 3½ miles distant.

Test pilot Don Malick during an experimental flight with a special wingless design, similar to a Lunar Module, for testing simulated landings on the moon.

The preparations for a manned flight to the moon have thus reached a decisive stage: the path and landing sites have been mapped, the latter by the work done by the Orbiters.

The Apollo project, designed to carry three American Astronauts to the moon, requires for its launch a "moon port." This was established on Merritts Island, Cape Kennedy. The vehicle assembly building for the Saturn rocket carrying the Apollo spacecraft has fifty-two floors and is 475 feet high. As far as its enclosed space is concerned, it is the largest structure in the world, surpassing even the Pyramid of Cheops. It has four parts to allow four Saturn V rockets to be assembled simultaneously. The rockets carrying the spaceship on top have to be transported from the interior of the giant hall to the launching pads over a distance of three and a half miles along the coast of Florida on a crawler tractor whose loading area is larger than five tennis courts.

Saturn V is approximately 370 feet tall, the first stage develops a thrust of 7·5 million pounds and is able to lift the giant booster rocket, weighing 2,819 tons, together with the Apollo spaceship, without difficulty. On its journey to the moon, the Apollo spaceship follows along the path of the Orbiters and then starts circling the moon. One lunar orbit takes two hours and then the final stage of the flight begins: two of the Astronauts transfer into the LM (Lunar Module) in which they attempt the descent to the lunar surface. The lunar module weighing approximately 16 tons is fitted with a rocket engine and carries sufficient fuel for a soft landing and subsequent take-off from the lunar surface. Special pressurized suits have been developed for stepping out into the vacuum existing on the moon. These suits have already been tested in vacuum chambers. Temperatures on the moon fluctuate between the extremes +120° C (noon) and −175° C (midnight,) making a stay there anything but comfortable. For that reason Man's first visit will be a brief one. After having completed their tasks (collecting lunar rocks, which are probably of basalt type, and making some measurements) the two Astronauts will embark in their lunar excursion module and steer towards the parking orbit of the Apollo spaceship, effect a rendezvous, and dock their LM to the Apollo spaceship. Then they will transfer into the Apollo spaceship. The Apollo spaceship will then enter into a transfer orbit to earth, the LM being left behind in a parking orbit around the moon.

Traveller between earth and Mars: The American Mars probe Mariner IV weighing 573 pounds prior to completion in the assembly room. During assembly work, the camera fitted in the center part is covered by protective shrouds. The two aerials can be seen at the back. Because of the greater distance between Mars and the sun, the solar paddles which provide electric power for operating the instruments and the transmitter are made especially large.

All this sounds very simple and matter-of-fact but the number of technological, mathematical and physical as well as human problems is enormous and only with the utmost care and with responsible preparation can an attempt be made to carry out this first really great space exercise by human beings.

A test flight of Saturn V with an unmanned Apollo capsule took place on November 9, 1967. Duration of flight: eight hours thirty-seven minutes. After two earth orbits at an altitude of 115 miles, an altitude of 10,600 miles was reached. During its return, the Apollo capsule was accelerated to 24,850 m.p.h., corresponding to the velocity during the return flight from the moon. The flight went as planned, the Apollo capsule landed undamaged 620 miles northwest of Hawaii, the heat shield being heated to a temperature of 2,800° C during re-entry into the earth's atmosphere.

On January 22, 1968 the first test of the Apollo lunar module took place. It lasted just under eight hours. In an earth orbit the guidance systems, retro-rockets for the descent to the lunar surface, the propulsion system of the last stage for take-off from the lunar surface, as well as the stage separation necessary for this test, were tried out. A second test of the Apollo lunar module took place on April 4, 1968. Owing to failure of the third stage (it failed to re-ignite,) this was only a partial success.

On October 11, an Apollo space capsule with the Astronauts Walter M. Schirra (Commander,) Don F. Eisele and R. Walter Cunningham aboard was launched by a Saturn I B rocket and placed into a low earth orbit. The flight was scheduled to last eleven days and was completed according to plan. Rendezvous maneuvers with the second stage of the Saturn I B carrier rocket were carried out and changes in orbit made with the aid of the propulsion system of the service module. Thus the original orbit with a perigee of 102 miles and apogee of 173 miles was changed to one with an apogee of 275 miles. The spacecraft returned to earth in the early afternoon, coming down in the Atlantic Ocean. This successful dress rehearsal for a manned flight to the moon and the flight of Soyus 3 have brought forward into the immediate future the realization of one of man's age-old dreams: to set foot on another celestial body.

After the success of the Apollo 7 flight, the Space Research Center

The Surveyor III "mini-dredger" at work on the moon.

decided, to the surprise of the public, to fix the date for the launching of Apollo 8—December 21, 1968. This time the Saturn V rocket was to be used and the destination was farther afield than ever before. It was planned to circle the moon, but in case of difficulty the program could have been changed during flight to either a long-distance flight between earth and the moon or a single circling of the moon before returning to earth. The spaceship was manned by Frank Borman (born 1928,) James A. Lovell (born 1928) and William A. Anders (born 1933.) The launching of the giant rocket took place on the appointed day, from Cape Kennedy. The flight went exactly according to plan and on December 24, 1968 Apollo 8 went into orbit round the moon. Whenever the spaceship passed behind the moon, communication with earth was interrupted and the Astronauts were unable to see the earth beyond the horizon of the moon. As even these parts of the flight exactly followed the schedule, the planned ten orbits of the moon at a height of approximately sixty-six miles could be carried out. William Anders as flight

This nearly vertical photograph from Apollo 8 covers an area of about 50 square miles on the far side of the moon. The shadowed crater in the middle is about 20 miles in diameter. The area shown is within a very large crater having a diameter of 250 miles. Its center is located at about 157° west longitude and 4° south latitude.

photographer was able to take unique pictures. Christmas Eve was spent in the spaceship, which was circling the moon as a tiny subsatellite. On December 25 the engines of the service module of Apollo 8 ignited and the spaceship started its return to earth. On December 27, when the sun had not yet risen at the landing site in the Pacific Ocean, near the Equator, Apollo 8 landed in the water exactly on target. The Astronauts were taken to the aircraft carrier U.S.S. *Yorktown* by helicopter. The

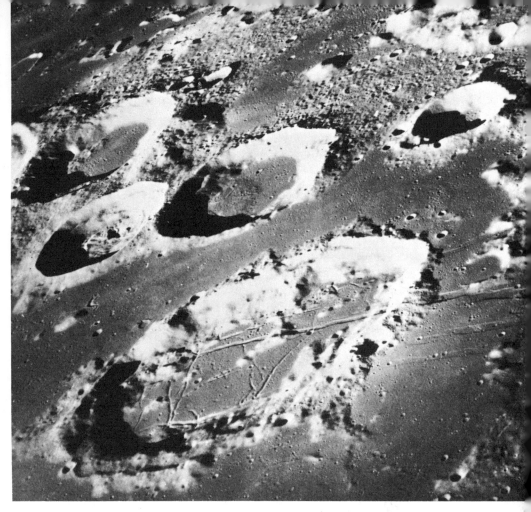

On Christmas Eve, 1968 the Apollo 8 crew photographed this moon crater from a distance of about 69 miles. In the foreground is the Goclenius crater (diameter 40 miles.) In the background to the left are Magelhaens, Magelhaens A and Colombo A.

world was tremendously impressed by the precision with which the flight had been accomplished. For the first time men were able to go beyond the immediate vicinity of the earth and a new era of space exploration was introduced.

This program was followed by a Russian project. On January 14 and 15, 1969, respectively, Soyus 4 with Cosmonaut Vladimir Shatalov, and Soyus 5 with three Cosmonauts, Boris Volynov, Yevgeny Khrunov and Alexei Yeliseyev were launched. On January 16 a docking maneuver took place. Soyus 4 had completed thirty-four orbits and Soyus 5 eighteen. Shortly afterward the two Soyus 5 co-pilots, Yeliseyev and Khrunov, left their spaceship and changed over to Soyus 4. The two spaceships were separated again after four and a half hours. The transfer maneuver had taken one hour. Both spaceships returned to earth and landed in Soviet territory, Soyus 4 on January 17 and Soyus 5 on January 18. This project can be considered as a preparation for a space station which will circle the earth on a satellite trajectory and be permanently manned by scientists, who will be relieved from time to time. Such a project was suggested in the early days of space flight, as many scientific studies can only be accomplished outside the Earth's atmosphere.

The flight of Soyus 4 and 5 was preceded by the flight of Soyus 3 as a final rehearsal with Giorgy Beregovoi. He executed a rendezvous maneuver with an unmanned spaceship, Soyus 2, which started on October 25, 1968 and finished on October 30 when the spaceship landed in Soviet territory.

The flight of Apollo 9 represented one of the last "dress rehearsals" for the planned start of Apollo 11 on July 17, 1969 with a landing by the Lunar Module on the surface of the moon on July 20. The Apollo 9 flight lasted from March 3 to March 13 and served primarily to test the LM maneuver in an earth orbit. On March 3 the LM left the third stage of the Saturn V rocket and on March 4 the Apollo spaceship changed course several times with the LM in docking position at a height of between 125 and 316 miles. On March 7 James McDivitt and Russell Schweickart, who had transferred to the LM, moved away to a distance of 63 miles from the spaceship in which David Scott remained. The flight of the LM lasted six hours. Apollo 9 returned to earth on March 13, 340 miles north of Puerto Rico, only one mile from the intended target.

In reply to the question often posed as to *why* we want to land on the moon, Dr. Wernher von Braun gave this answer: "We do not expect to find gold or uranium on the moon, but we do expect that in the course of development of the technology necessary for our lunar expedition we will learn so much that the practical application of the knowledge and experience gained thereby in other more lucrative fields will not only cover the cost of the project but will create new values."

Looking at Other Planets

Owing to the absence of any atmosphere, the moon does not provide a suitable environment for highly developed organic life, although according to the most recent observations it is not yet a completely dead world. Venus and Mars are different. Both possess an atmosphere; that of Venus is so dense that its cloud cover obscures the view of the actual surface of the planet. On the other hand, Mars has a very rarefied atmosphere which only occasionally shows the formation of clouds. The size of Venus is almost exactly the same as that of earth, with a diameter of approximately 7,600 miles. The surface of Venus is 98 per cent. of the earth's surface and its mass 81·5 per cent. of the earth's mass. The surface of Venus reflects 61 per cent. of the sunlight reaching it but this is more or less all we know with certainty about this strange planet. The secret of Venus cannot be solved from earth, either with the aid of our largest telescopes or by radio astronomy. The answer can be obtained only by probes dispatched into the near vicinity or to the planet itself. The first successful attempt was undertaken by the Americans with their Mariner II launched on August 27, 1962. The probe weighing 443 pounds passed Venus on December 14 of the same year at a distance of 21,000 miles and transmitted data to earth from a distance of 36,000,000 miles. According to information radioed by Mariner II, the surface temperature of Venus is believed to be $+400°$ C. The clouds are very high, their base is thought to be forty-five miles above the planet's surface, the temperature at the cloud base is assumed to be approximately $+90°$ C and at the top $=55°$ C. It is certain that Venus has no magnetic field; this would indicate a very slow rotation of the planet. The flight of Mariner II, very successful as far as accuracy of aim was concerned, yielded rather limited results and still left the mystery of Venus unsolved. Two Russian probes, Venus 2 and Venus 3, launched on November 12 and 16, 1965 respectively, did not produce any further results. Venus 2 flew past the planet on February 27, 1963 and Venus 3 even made a hard landing on Venus, thus scoring a direct hit. Unfortunately (and it is remarkable that this happened in both cases) radio contact was lost on approaching Venus. The solution of the mysteries surrounding Venus will therefore have to be attempted by further probes. It is worth mentioning that suitable launching dates for a flight to Venus recur only every nineteen months.

The Venus 4 and Mariner V space probes (see table) generally confirmed earlier results. Venus 4 even soft landed on the surface of Venus, but radio contact was lost on landing. For a period of thirty-four hours Mariner V radioed back to earth a flood of scientific data about the atmosphere, temperature, luminous phenomena, etc. of the planet Venus. The final evaluation of the Mariner V results shows that the atmospheric pressure on the surface of Venus appears to be 75–100 atm —four to five times as much as the figure announced by the Russian astronomers on the basis of the Venus IV results. The assumption therefore is that the Russian Sonde must either have landed on an undiscovered 15-mile high peak, or the transmission of data was interrupted at about that height. The surface temperature is put by the American experts at 500° C, and announced by the Russians to be 270° C upward—too high to permit any forms of life similar to those which have developed on earth.

Good conditions for flights to Mars recur only every twenty-six months. With the flight of Mariner IV, the Americans succeeded in one of the most spectacular long-distance reconnaissance missions. It was a tremendous achievement of space research. The probe, weighing 577 pounds and fitted with four solar panels (solar batteries,) was launched on November 28, 1964 by an Atlas Agena rocket and reached Mars on July 14, 1965 after a journey of almost eight months, involving a midcourse correction controlled by radio signals. A television camera started transmitting at a distance of 8,000 miles from Mars and completed transmission at a distance of 6,000 miles. At that time the distance between Mars and earth was 138 million miles. The diameter of Mars is only 4,200 miles compared with earth's diameter of 7,918 miles, its surface is barely one-third of the earth's surface but a Martian day lasts twenty-four hours thirty-seven minutes twenty-three seconds and is therefore slightly longer than a day on earth. From earth we can see white polar caps from time to time during the winter season on the

A "ride" in space. Astronaut Richard Gordon riding on the nose of Gemini 11 in order to reach the docked Agena target satellite. Above him the radar aerial of the Agena rocket, on the left the earth, on the right the open hatch of the Gemini capsule. This "ride" took place 185 miles above the earth's surface.

respective Mars hemisphere. Dark spots on Mars showing changes in colour and sometimes also in shape appear to be connected with the seasons. Owing to the inclination of its axis of twenty-five degrees, Mars has a sequence of seasons similar to that of earth but the seasons are longer than here because the duration of one Martian year is 687 earth days.

The transmission of television pictures from Mars was a masterpiece of telecommunications. Each picture was resolved into 200 lines, each line in turn into 200 image points so that each picture was made up from a total of 40,000 image points. The picture halftone of each point was transmitted to earth in the form of a numerical code. Each picture required a transmission time of eight hours twelve minutes, each picture point travelling approximately twelve minutes from Mars to earth. The pictures were stored in the probe on tape and were transmitted to our ground station only in response to a command signal received from earth. Mariner IV transmitted fourteen perfectly focused close-up television pictures of the Mars surface to the Pasadena tracking station. One of the most interesting results, the great surprise produced by this robot expedition, was the discovery that the photographed Mars area is surprisingly similar to the lunar landscape. Mars, too, has craters; altogether seventy of them were noticed with diameters ranging from three to seventy-five miles, with walls several hundred yards high and depths reaching up to two and a half miles. However, Mariner IV has photographed only 1 per cent. of the entire Mars surface and it is therefore not possible to draw any general conclusions concerning conditions on Mars.

The various instruments carried by Mariner IV provided a further valuable result. Mars has no magnetic field and it can therefore be assumed that it does not have an iron core. This assumption agrees very well with its low average specific gravity (3·95.) The atmospheric pressure on the planet's surface corresponds to atmospheric pressure on earth at altitudes of seventeen to nineteen miles, the Martian atmosphere being assumed to consist of 72 per cent. nitrogen, 16 per cent. carbon dioxide, 18 per cent. argon and only traces of water vapour and oxygen. The power of the instrument data and picture information reaching earth was only one-ten-trillionth part of one Watt with an output of 10 Watts.

According to data supplied by Mariner IV, Mars is indeed not an hospitable world (a fact known to astronomers for some time) with very low night temperatures and noon temperatures only slightly above freezing. It was not the purpose of Mariner IV to search for traces of life on Mars, and it was not its purpose to solve the puzzle of extra-terrestrial life. The real search for life on the small, reddish orange shiny planet will commence only during the next approaches of the planet. For these research projects work is going ahead in the U.S.A. on an unmanned spaceship named "Voyager" which is intended to make a soft landing on Mars and search its surface automatically for any organic substances.

Let us revert once again to Mariner IV. After its fly-by of Mars, the probe entered a planetary orbit around the sun and maintained radio

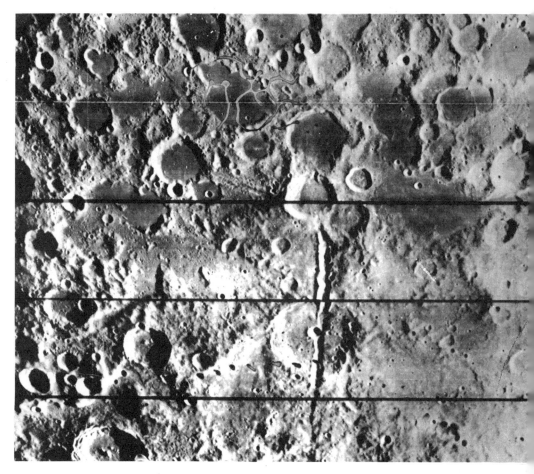

A "crack" in the moon. A fault approximately 150 miles wide on the reverse side of the moon cutting through some of the older craters. In its turn it is cut by a smaller crater of more recent date. This picture was taken by Lunar Orbiter IV on May 11, 1967.

contact with the ground station up to the beginning of October, 1965. In Spring 1966, Mariner once again approached earth and at the end of May the Goldstone tracking station in California was able to resume contact with the probe, recording a number of scientific data. The renewed contact also showed that on its long interplanetary journey the probe has not suffered any accidents and had not collided with any meteorites.

For 1969 NASA are planning two Mars fly-bys with Mariner F

and G. Mariner F (= Mariner V when successful) was launched on February 25 and Mariner G (= Mariner VI) on March 28. The latter will fly by at a distance of 2,000 miles from the surface of Mars and reach our "next door" planet on August 5. Pictures with a resolution of about 900 feet will be transmitted by television. Mariner V will fly over the equatorial regions and Mariner VI over the southern polar regions of Mars. The optimum launch window occurs between the middle of February and the middle of April. The arrival times on Mars will probably be only five days apart and are due about the end of July or the beginning of August. Weight of the probes: 880 pounds.

In spite of the outstanding successes which followed each other in a breathtaking sequence, we are only at the beginning of the space age, in a position roughly similar to that of aviation in 1920; the great era of space travel still lies ahead.

The 1970s will probably not be dominated by a single project, such as the U.S.A. Apollo programme for landing a man on the moon, which was the most important target during the 1960s. Attention will above all be concentrated on the exploration of the solar system. However, space flights in the vicinity of earth will also play an important part, involving the exploitation of space technology for practical purposes. Automation and instrumentation will reach new levels of perfection as a result of man's increasingly sophisticated talents in the fields of remote control and telemetry, as well as the dramatic improvement in the reliability of the system concerned.

Principal Artificial Satellites

Name	Launch date	Decayed	Weight in pounds approx	Period mins	Perigee in miles approx	Apogee in miles approx	Remarks
Sputnik I	4. 10. 57	Early January 1958	174	96·2	143	591	First artificial satellite
Sputnik II	3. 11. 57	14. 4. 58	1,113	103·7	141	1,046	Dog Laika on board
Explorer I	1. 2. 58	—	31	105	213	1,032	First American satellite
Vanguard I	17. 3. 58	—	3½	134·3	411	2,469	Still transmitting
Sputnik III	15. 5. 58	6. 4. 60	2,919	106	136	1,174	Made valuable contributions to the International Geophysical year
Score	18. 12. 58	21. 1. 59	8,730	101·5	111	876	First successful telecommunications experiment
Explorer VI	7. 8. 59	July, 61 (?)	141½	750	157	26,562	Travelled far out from earth. Explored the Van Allen belt more closely
Explorer VII	13. 10. 59	—	91½	101·2	346	677	Miniature laboratory between the outermost layers of atmosphere and space
Tiros I	1. 4. 60	—	275	99·2	441	470	First weather observation satellite
Sputnik IV	14. 5. 60	7. 10. 60	9,988	91·1	190	230	"Spaceship 1" unmanned, with pressurized cabin and air conditioning equipment
Discoverer XIII	10. 8. 60	10. 8. 60	300	94·1	162	439	First successful return and recovery of a satellite
Echo I	12. 8. 60	May, 68	167	118·3	951	1,056	First balloon satellite
Sputnik V	19. 8. 60	20. 8. 60	10,120	90·7	191	212	"Spaceship 2" carrying two dogs successful re-entry. First step towards

Principal Artificial Satellites cont.

Name	Launch date	Decayed	Weight in pounds approx	Period mins	Perigee in miles approx	Apogee in miles approx	Remarks
							manned space flight
Courier I B	4. 10. 60	—	499	107	507	662	Improved communications satellite
Tiros II	23. 11. 60	—	279	98·2	389	456	Second weather observation satellite
Tiros III	12. 6. 61	—	284	100·3	458	514	Third weather observation satellite
Tiros IV	8. 2. 62	—	284	100·3	443	527	Fourth weather observation satellite
Ariel	26. 4. 62	—	132	100·9	246	762	First international instrument satellite
Tiros V	19. 7. 62	—	286	100·5	364	612	Fifth weather observation satellite. Area of observation extended as far as Greenland and Arctic
Telstar I	10. 7. 62	—	169	157·6	590	3,524	First television commercial satellite. Not responding to commands since Nov. 30, 1962
Tiros VI	18. 9. 62	—	284	98·7	423	449	Sixth weather observation satellite
Explorer XIV	2. 10. 62	—	98	2,185	1,043	60,706	Satellite on an extremely elliptic orbit. Principal object: radiation measurements
Anna I B	31. 10. 62	—	347½	107·8	679	733	"Flashlight satellite" for geodetic measurements
Relay I	13. 12. 62	—	171½	185	823	4,052	Telecommunications satellite. On Jan. 17, 1963

Name	Launch date	Decayed	Weight in pounds approx	Period mins	Perigee in miles approx	Apogee in miles approx	Remarks
							first regular programs from commercial radio stations transmitted via Relay I
Syncom I	14. 2. 63	—	147½	1,426·4	21,366	23,135	First communications satellite in a "stationary" orbit. Radio link failed
Telstar II	7. 5. 63	—	174½	225·2	609	6,750	Second commercial television satellite
Tiros VII	19. 6. 63	—	295	97·4	386	409	Seventh weather observation satellite
Syncom II	26. 7. 63	—	145	1,454·1	22,240	22,933	Was successfully stabilized in a "stationary" orbit. Radio link working perfectly. Facilitates teleprinter, telephone and facsimile radio transmission via space
Polyot I	1. 11. 63	—	?		212	370	Fully maneuverable, unmanned spaceship. Changed to an orbit with a perigee of 213 miles and an apogee of 893 miles. The initial period of this orbit was 102·5 minutes
Centaur II	27. 11. 63	—	11,023	108	368	1,058	Hydrogen rocket placed 5-ton satellite into orbit
Tiros VIII	21. 12. 63	—	286	99·3	438	471	First weather observation satellite of the

Principal Artificial Satellites cont.

Name	Launch date	Decayed	Weight in pounds approx	Period mins	Perigee in miles approx	Apogee in miles approx	Remarks
							Tiros series with a new picture transmission system enabling the reception of cloud pictures even with simpler ground equipment
Echo II	25. 1. 64	—	572	108·8	629	836	Second balloon satellite, diameter 135 ft.
SA–5	29. 1. 64	—	37,478	94·8	164	468	Up to now the heaviest object in orbit. Testing of first and second stage of Saturn I
Electron I and II	30. 1. 64	—	?	166 / 1,360	252 / 263	4,449 / 42,504	Two Russian satellites placed into different orbits with the same carrier rocket
Gemini capsule	8. 4. 64	12. 4. 64	6,614	90·8	75	153	Unmanned Gemini capsule in orbit. Carrier rocket with a thrust of 250 tons
Apollo capsule	28. 5. 64	2. 6. 64	17,637	88	112	141	Unmanned Apollo capsule in orbit. Launch vehicle 2-stage Saturn rocket
Sentry	17. 7. 64	—	?	5,760	57,500	57,000	Two satellites, first placed into an elliptic orbit (230 miles to 62,500 miles from earth) and then stabilized in a circular orbit. Nuclear detection satellites. Angular spacing 130°
Syncom III	19. 8. 64	—	81½	1,436	22,500	22,500	The second fully

Name	Launch date	Decayed	Weight in pounds approx	Period mins	Perigee in miles approx	Apogee in miles approx	Remarks
							operational communications satellite in a stationary orbit at a distance from earth of approx. 23,000 miles. The satellite covers the Pacific and transmits television, telephone and teleprint traffic between U.S.A. and Japan. Was used for the direct transmission from the Olympic games in Tokyo to N. America. Still operating
Pegasus I	16. 2. 65	—	3,300	98·6	430	445	A giant satellite weighing 1½ tons, visible with the naked eye, fitted with two flat "wings" for measuring cosmic dust. At the same time the eighth successive launch of the giant Saturn I rocket in this series. Still active
SNAP–10A	3. 4. 65	—	246½	112	812	812	First launch of a nuclear reactor for exploring the suitability of reactor propulsion in space. Output 500 W. Transmissions ceased May 21, 1965
Early Bird	6. 4. 65	—	83½	1,436	22,500	22,500	First satellite

Name	Launch date	Decayed	Weight in pounds approx	Period mins	Perigee in miles approx	Apogee in miles approx	Remarks
							for commercial television, telephone, radio and teleprinter communication between North America and Europe. First satellite within the framework of the planned, world-wide satellite network in which 41 countries, including the U.S.A., are engaged. Stationary satellite orbiting the earth at a height of approximately 23,000 miles at the speed of the earth's rotation, over the equatorial Atlantic
ESSA–1	3. 2. 66	—	305	100·2	434	524	The first satellite of the Tiros operation system. A weather satellite of type Tiros whose orbits take it over the vicinity of the polar regions. Fitted both with normal cameras as well as an infrared camera for photographing the cloud cover over virtually the whole earth in daylight and darkness. The

Principal Artificial Satellites cont.

Name	Launch date	Decayed	Weight in pounds approx	Period mins	Perigee in miles approx	Apogee in miles approx	Remarks
							daylight photographs were suitable also for direct transmission via the APT automatic picture transmission system to each of the ground stations over which the satellite passed. Camera went out of action on July 27, 1966
Nimbus 2	15. 5. 66	—	908½	108	687	737	Picture-taking weather satellite in a polar orbit, transmitting for the first time night pictures of cloud cover direct to the ground stations
Lani-Bird	11. 1. 67	—	189	1,436	22,500	22,500	This communica-tions satellite was stabilized above the date line (180th meridian) and acts as a bridge spanning the Pacific Ocean. It connects the extreme west of the U.S.A. with east Asia, Australia and N. Zealand. Power supply provided by 12,756 silicon solar cells giving an output of 85 W
Biosatellite 2	7. 9. 67	—	286	90	187	196	Brought down prematurely after 17 orbits (44 hr. 54 min. in orbit).

Principal Artificial Satellites cont.

Name	Launch date	Decayed	Weight in pounds approx	Period mins	Perigee in miles approx	Apogee in miles approx	Remarks
Cosmos 186 Cosmos 188	} 30. 10. 67	—	?		131 125	147 172	Amoeba, bacteria, plants, frog spawn, etc. on board First successful automatic docking maneuver
Esro II (Iris)	17. 5. 68	—	176	89	204	674	First satellite of the European Space Research Organization (ESRO)
Explorer 38	4. 7. 68	—	416	230	3,730	3,730	Radio astronomy research satellite, recorded for the first time, with the aid of two extra long aerials (1,660 ft. each), low-frequency radio emission from the Sun, Jupiter and Milky Way, which cannot be observed from earth because of reflection by the ionosphere
Proton 4	16. 11. 68	—	37,478	91·5	159	309	Research satellite
OAO	8. 12. 68	—	4,365	99	478	478	Orbital Astronomical Observatory. With its 11 telescopes it is able to make astronomical observations outside the atmosphere. Telescopes used are not light telescopes but instruments mainly for registering

Principal Artificial Satellites cont.

Name	Launch date	Decayed	Weight in pounds approx	Period mins	Perigee in miles approx	Apogee in miles approx	Remarks
							X rays and the wavelengths of ultraviolet rays as well as radio frequencies

The above list includes only the most important satellites, mainly those intended for new tasks. The total number of artificial satellites launched up to the middle of 1968 is more than 350 but cannot be determined accurately because of a number of secret launches. The Soviet Union alone launched no fewer than 261 satellites in the "Cosmos" series between March 16, 1962 and the end of December, 1968. The inclination of their orbits varies between 33 and 90° relative to the plane of the earth's equator. An inclination of 90° means that the satellite travels along the polar route, passing over North and South Pole. A satellite in such an orbit passes in due course over all points on the earth's surface.

Manned Space Flights

Name of spaceship	Country	Date	Astronaut	Number of orbits	Duration of flight hr. min.	Remarks
Vostok 1	U.S.S.R.	12. 4. 61	Gagarin	1	1 48	Killed in an air crash on March 27, 1968
Vostok 2	U.S.S.R.	5/6. 5. 61	Titov	17	25 18	
Friendship 7	U.S.A.	20. 2. 62	Glenn	3	4 55	
Aurora 7	U.S.A.	24. 5. 62	Carpenter	3	4 56	
Vostok 3	U.S.S.R.	11/15. 8. 62	Nikolayev	64	94 22	
Vostok 4	U.S.S.R.	12/15. 8. 62	Popovich	48	70 57	
Sigma 7	U.S.A.	3. 10.62	Schirra	6	9 13	
Faith 7	U.S.A.	15/16. 5. 63	Cooper	22	34 20	
Vostok 5	U.S.S.R.	14/19. 6. 63	Bykovski	81	119 6	
Vostok 6	U.S.S.R.	16/19. 6. 63	Tereshkova	48	70 50	
Voskhod 1	U.S.S.R.	12/13. 10. 64	Feoktistov Komarov Yegorov	16	24 17	
Voskhod 2	U.S.S.R.	18/19. 3. 65	Belyayev Leonov	17	26 2	Leonov carried out the first walk in space, duration 20 min.
Gemini 3	U.S.A.	23. 3. 65	Grissom Young	3	4 53	

Manned Space Flights cont.

Name of spaceship	Country	Date	Astronaut	Number of orbits	Duration of flight hr. min.	Remarks
Gemini 4	U.S.A.	3/7. 6. 65	McDivitt White	62	97 56	White's space walk lasted 21 min.
Gemini 5	U.S.A.	21/29. 8. 65	Cooper Conrad	120	190 56	
Gemini 7	U.S.A.	4/18. 12. 65	Borman Lovell	206	330 35	To date the longest space flight, duration 13 days, 18 hr. 35 min.
Gemini 6	U.S.A.	15/16. 12. 65	Schirra Stafford	15	25 51	Rendezvous maneuver with Gemini 7, approach to a distance of approximately 6 ft.
Gemini 8	U.S.A.	16. 3. 66	Armstrong Scott	6½	10 42	Successful docking maneuver with Agena target satellite
Gemini 9	U.S.A.	3/6. 6. 66	Stafford Cernan	44	72 22	Cernan left the spacecraft for 2 hr. 5 min.
Gemini 10	U.S.A.	18/21. 7. 66	Young Collins	43	70 47	Collins left spacecraft for 30 min. Apogee 472 miles
Gemini 11	U.S.A.	12/15. 9. 66	Conrad Gordon	44	71 17	Gordon left spacecraft for 44 min., Gemini 11 and the Agena reached a record altitude of 845 miles.
Gemini 12	U.S.A.	11/14. 11. 66	Lovell Aldrin	59	94 37	Aldrin left spacecraft for 2 hr. 9 min. Photographs taken from open capsule for 3 hr. 21 min.
Soyus 1	U.S.S.R.	23/24. 4. 67	Komarov	16	24	Fatal accident during landing owing to failure of braking parachute
Apollo 7	U.S.A.	11/22. 10. 68	Schirra Eisele Cunningham	164	261 40	To test the Apollo capsule and its service module

Manned Space Flights cont.

Name of spaceship	Country	Date	Astronaut	Number of orbits	Duration of flight hr. min.	Remarks
						propulsion system. Rendezvous maneuver with the second stage of Saturn IB carrier rocket. Apogee 292 miles
Soyus 3	U.S.S.R.	26/30. 10. 68	Beregovoi	63	94 51	Spaceship executed rendezvous maneuvers with unmanned Soyus 2 launched 25. 10. 68
Apollo 8	U.S.A.	21/27. 12. 68	Borman Lovell Anders	—	172	First flight to moon circling moon ten times
Soyus 4	U.S.S.R.	14/17. 1. 69	Shatalov			Link-up and transfer maneuvers during satellite trajectory around the earth. Height of trajectory between 130 and 158 miles
Soyus 5	U.S.S.R.	15/18. 1. 69	Volynov Khrunov Yeliseyev			
Apollo 9	U.S.A.	3/13. 3. 69	McDivitt Scott Schweickart	162	240	Successful test of LM in earth orbit.

Moon Probes

Name	Date of launch	Country	Remarks
Lunik II	12. 9. 59	U.S.S.R.	Weight 33,300 pounds, impacted in *Mare Imbrium* on Sept. 13. No instruments on board apart from radio transmitter
Lunik III	4. 10. 59	U.S.S.R.	Flight round the moon. First photographs of the reverse side of the moon from a distance of 37,000 to 43,000 miles
Ranger IV	23. 4. 62	U.S.A.	Retro-rockets failed, crashed on the moon
Ranger VI	30. 1. 64	U.S.A.	Impacted on Feb. 2 in the Sea of Tranquillity. Television cameras failed
Ranger VII	28. 7. 64	U.S.A.	Impacted on July 31 in *Mare Cognitum*. The six

Moon Probes cont.

Name	Date of launch	Country	Remarks
			television cameras returned 4,316 close-ups of the lunar surface
Ranger VIII	17. 2. 65	U.S.A.	Probe weighing 808·8 pounds impacted on Feb. 20 in the Sea of Tranquillity. Television cameras transmitted back to earth 7,137 pictures
Ranger IX	21. 1. 65	U.S.A.	Impacted on March 24 in the Crater Alphonsus, 6,150 television photographs. Ranger project concluded with Ranger IX
Luna 5	9. 5. 65	U.S.S.R.	Unsuccessful soft landing of the spacecraft weighing 3,250 pounds
Sonde 3	18. 7. 65	U.S.S.R.	Two million square miles of the reverse of the moon photographed on July 20 from a distance of 7,200 to 6,200 miles
Luna 7	4. 10. 65	U.S.S.R.	Unsuccessful soft landing of the spacecraft weighing 3,313 pounds
Luna 8	3. 12. 65	U.S.S.R.	Unsuccessful soft landing of the spacecraft weighing 3,358 pounds. Transmitting equipment failed
Luna 9	31. 1. 66	U.S.S.R.	Soft landed on February 3, in *Oceanus Procellarum*. First television pictures transmitted from the perspective of the lunar surface
Luna 10	31. 3. 66	U.S.S.R.	First moon satellite, Periselenum 235 miles, Aposelenum 612 miles. Period 2 hr. 58 min. No optical instruments on board
Surveyor I	30. 5. 66	U.S.A.	The spacecraft weighing 2,191 pounds soft landed at a distance of 590 miles from Luna 9, in *Oceanus Procellarum*. High-quality television pictures transmitted
Lunar Orbiter I	10. 8. 66	U.S.A.	Transmitted among other information the first picture of earth as seen from the moon
Luna 11	24. 8. 66	U.S.S.R.	The spacecraft weighing 3,616 pounds circles the moon in 2 hr. 58 min. Periselenum 100 miles, Aposelenum 750 miles. No optical instruments on board
Surveyor II	23. 9. 66	U.S.A.	After a flight of 62 hr. 46 min. duration, crashed owing to failure of the retro-rocket system
Luna 12	22. 10. 66	U.S.S.R.	First Russian orbiter with photographic equipment on board
Lunar Orbiter II	6. 11. 66	U.S.A.	Circling the moon. Periselenum approximately 30 miles. Provided the first close-up picture of the Crater Copernicus on November 23
Luna 13	21. 12. 66	U.S.S.R.	Soft landed in the *Oceanus Procellarum* on Dec. 24. Selanographic latitude 18° 52′, longitude 62° 03′. Television pictures transmitted
Lunar Orbiter III	5. 2. 67	U.S.A.	Circling the moon. Periselenum approximately 30 miles. The photographic cameras of the Orbiter search for suitable landing sites on the moon
Surveyor III	17. 4. 67	U.S.A.	Soft landed on April 19 in the *Oceanus Procellarum*. Moon surface investigated by mini-dredger

Moon Probes cont.

Name	Date of launch	Country	Remarks
Lunar Orbiter IV	4. 5. 67	U.S.A.	Provides data for a general photographic chart of the moon, including the reverse side
Surveyor IV	14. 7. 67	U.S.A.	Radio contact lost on ignition of retro-rockets
Lunar Orbiter V	1. 8. 67	U.S.A.	Up to now the best pictures of the reverse side of the moon taken from a distance of 1,600 miles. Intended to photograph 90% of the lunar surface
Surveyor V	8. 9. 67	U.S.A.	Soft landed in the Sea of Tranquillity on Sept. 11. The structure of moon rocks was chemically analyzed by bombarding the surface of the moon with alpha rays and observing their interaction with the atomic nuclei of the moon's surface. The following results were obtained: Carbon less than 3%; Oxygen approx. 58%; Sodium less than 2%; Magnesium approx. 3%; Aluminum approx. 6·5%; Silicon approx. 18·5%; Sulphur, iron, cobalt, nickel, approx. 13%; Elements heavier than nickel: less than 0·5%. This indicates rock type similar to basalt
Surveyor VI	9. 11. 67	U.S.A.	Soft landed in *Sinus Medii*. Performed a sideways jump of 13 ft.
Surveyor VII	7. 1. 68	U.S.A.	Soft landed 20 miles north of crater Tycho in rugged terrain. Transmitted 21,000 television pictures during first two weeks after landing. Chemical analysis of lunar surface at that point revealed that the material examined is completely different from any type of rock known on earth. Specific gravity, as well as content of iron and heavy metals were found to be less
Luna 14	7. 4. 68	U.S.S.R.	Orbiting the moon at an altitude ranging from 100 to 540 miles
Sonde 5	15. 9. 68	U.S.S.R.	The automatic space station orbited the moon, approaching the lunar surface to within 1,210 miles, and returned to earth where it splashed down in the Indian Ocean on September 21, and was picked up by a Soviet recovery vessel on Sept. 22
Sonde 6	10. 11. 68	U.S.S.R.	The unmanned spacecraft circled the moon at a distance of 1,512 miles and returned to earth on November 17. Believed to have studied the influence of cosmic rays on humans

The above list does not include those spacecraft which missed the moon.

Flights to Other Planets

Name	Date of launch	Country	Remarks
Mariner II	27. 8. 62	U.S.A.	The probe weighing 443 pounds passed Venus on December 14, 1962 at a distance of 21,000 miles, test data being transmitted from a distance of 36 million miles. Radio contact maintained up to a distance of 54 million miles
Mariner IV	28. 11. 64	U.S.A.	The probe weighing 573 pounds passed the surface of Mars on July 15, 1965 at a distance of 6,200 miles. 14 very clear television close-ups transmitted to earth over a distance of 130 million miles. Radio contact would have been possible over a distance of 210 million miles. Radio contact re-established toward the end of May, 1966
Venus 3	16. 11. 65	U.S.S.R.	The probe weighing 2,116 pounds reached the surface of Venus on March 1, 1966. Radio contact lost shortly before that
Venus 4	12. 6. 67	U.S.S.R.	The probe weighing 2,438 pounds soft landed on Venus on October 18, 1967. It recorded a surface temperature of 500° C. and a CO_2 content between 80 % and 95 %
Mariner V	14. 6. 67	U.S.A.	Flew by the surface of Venus at a distance of 2,477 miles on October 19, 1967. Recorded a brightly shining hydrogen corona and found a lower CO_2 content (72 %–87 %) than the Russian Venus 4 probe
Venus 5	5. 1. 69	U.S.S.R.	A probe weighing 2,486 pounds is intended to make a soft landing on Venus in May, 1969 and to give further information about density and temperature. (Mariner V showed that the atmosphere is so dense that the surface pressure is over 300 pounds per square inch – 22 times the normal pressure on earth. The temperature is approx. 500° C.)
Venus 6	10. 1. 69	U.S.S.R.	Intended to make a soft landing on Venus in May, 1969
Mariner VI	25. 2. 69	U.S.A.	Fly-by of Mars (see text)
Mariner VII	28. 3. 69	U.S.A.	Fly-by of Mars (see text)

*Printed Offset Litho in Great Britain by Cox & Wyman Ltd,
London, Fakenham and Reading*